PANAMA'S ECONOMIC DEVELOPMENT: THE ROLE OF AGRICULTURE

WILLIAM C. MERRILL
LEHMAN B. FLETCHER
RANDALL A. HOFFMANN
MICHAEL J. APPLEGATE

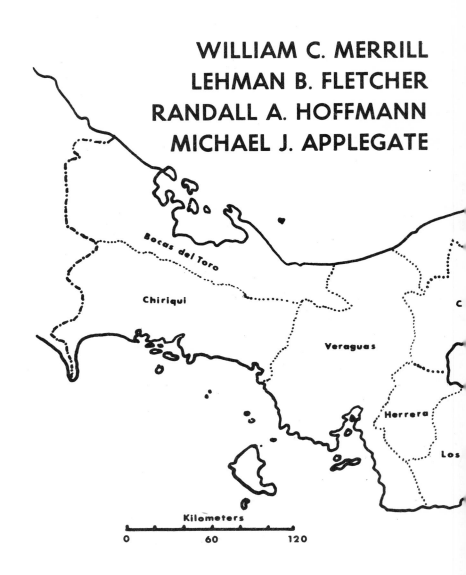

Bocas del Toro

Chiriqui

Veraguas

Herrera

C

Los

Kilometers

0   60   120

PANAMA'S
ECONOMIC
DEVELOPMENT:
THE ROLE
OF
AGRICULTURE

The Iowa State University Press, Ames, Iowa, U.S.A.

To ANNA LOU

The authors hold the following positions:

WILLIAM C. MERRILL, Professor of Economics, Iowa State University
LEHMAN B. FLETCHER, Professor of Economics, Iowa State University
RANDALL A. HOFFMANN, Associate Professor of Economics, Iowa State University
MICHAEL J. APPLEGATE, Assistant Professor of Economics, Oklahoma State University

© 1975 The Iowa State University Press
Ames, Iowa 50010. All rights reserved

First edition, 1975

Library of Congress Cataloging in Publication Data

Main entry under title:

Panama's economic development.

    Bibliography: p.
    1. Agriculture—Economic aspects—Panama.
2. Agriculture and state—Panama.   I. Merrill,
William Charles, 1934–
HD1822.P35   338.1′09862   74–16435
ISBN 0–8138–1205–4

CONTENTS

v

PREFACE

Panama's agricultural development was studied intensely by specialists during the 1970–73 period. Numerous reports on agricultural production, marketing, resource availability, and price policies were written by personnel from various agencies of the Government of Panama (GOP), the University of Panama, and international organizations. Much of this work was done in cooperation with or under the sponsorship of the Sector Study Commission (SSC) which was established at the National Planning Office and assigned responsibility for drafting a long-range agricultural development program. The commission's work was conducted in three phases. The first step was to collect and evaluate all available data related to Panama's agricultural development. This activity provided the SSC a general overview of the agricultural sector and allowed it to identify areas in which additional data and research were needed. Second, various government agencies and international organizations were asked to assist the commission with this research. Most of the studies prepared in this second phase were treated as working documents and were not distributed widely; nevertheless, these reports represent the major component of the agricultural sector study.

The third phase of SSC work began in September 1972. The goal of this phase was to summarize the reports prepared during phase two and to relate their various program proposals, recommendations, and information to the general agricultural situation. This book represents the results of phase three.

Although we have drawn heavily on the written reports of many persons who worked on various aspects of the sector study, we also have taken the liberty of revising, updating, and, in general, exercising considerable editorial discretion in presenting their findings. We hope that, in those cases where changes have been made, the authors will recognize the basis for making them. Readers with interests in specialized areas, or with questions about particular conclusions or findings, will need to consult the basic documents referenced throughout this book and in the bibliography. These documents contain more specific recommendations and information than can be presented in any summarization.

In preparing the basic reports for the sector study, most researchers worked with considerable understanding of their areas of specialization but lacked a detailed overview of the relative importance of different agricultural products, the changes taking place in the rural infrastructure, or the role that agriculture has played in Panama's development. As a result, it frequently was necessary for them to assume that the financial and human resources necessary to solve a particular problem or to implement a new program would be or could be available. This assumption is reasonable from the specialist's viewpoint when his suggestions involve

THE PANAMA CANAL IS AN IMPORTANT FACTOR IN PANAMA'S RAPID ECONOMIC GROWTH. (PHOTO: PANAMA TOURIST INSTITUTE)

MODERN SUPERMARKETS ARE POPULAR SHOPPING PLACES IN PANAMA CITY. (PHOTO: W. C. MERRILL)

BOTH RETAILERS AND CONSUMERS RELY ON THE CENTRAL PUBLIC MARKET IN PANAMA CITY FOR HIGH-QUALITY FRUITS AND VEGETABLES. (PHOTO: W. C. MERRILL)

relatively minor changes in or enlargements of existing programs. However, the assumption of unlimited resources is not realistic when all the recommendations in the various reports are considered. Panama simply does not have the resources to implement the thousands of recommendations contained in the many studies prepared for the SSC. Someone will have to assign priorities and decide how best to use the limited resources available.

In early 1973, the Government of Panama began a major reorganization of the Ministry of Agriculture and Livestock (MAG), the Institute of Economic Development (IFE), and several other agencies responsible for agricultural development programs. In this book, we generally have taken the governmental organization as it existed in December 1972 as the reference point when describing which agencies are (were) responsi-

GOVERNMENT STORES SELL STAPLE FOODS AT LOW PRICES. (PHOTO: W. C. MERRILL)

THE NATIONAL AGRICULTURAL SCHOOL AT DIVISA EMPHASIZES LEARNING BY DOING. (PHOTO: W. C. MERRILL)

ble for various programs. We may state, for example, that "the soil improvement program is carried out by MAG" or that "IFE provides credit to small farmers." Such statements accurately describe the situation that existed in December 1972. By June 1973, however, MAG had become the Ministry of Agricultural Development (MIDA) and IFE's agricultural credit programs were being transferred to the new Agricultural Development Bank. As a result, some sections of this book will

PANAMA'S TRADITIONS AND HISTORY ARE REFLECTED IN ITS COLORFUL COSTUMES AND DANCES. (PHOTO: PANAMA TOURIST INSTITUTE)

AGRARIAN REFORM SEEKS TO INCREASE SMALL FARMERS' INCOMES THROUGH COLLECTIVE ACTION. (PHOTO: W. C. MERRILL)

(OPPOSITE) THE GOVERNMENT SEEKS TO IMPROVE RURAL WELFARE AS WELL AS TO INCREASE FOOD PRODUCTION. (PHOTO: W. C. MERRILL)

appear to be somewhat behind Panama's rapidly changing administrative structure.

Our guiding objective in preparing this book is to provide the reader with a benchmark study that illustrates the role agriculture has played in Panama's development. Our observations and analysis on what has been happening in the agricultural sector, what is likely to happen, how well various programs have worked, and what programs or policies could help Panama achieve specific goals are not intended as criticisms of past or present policies or programs. Panama has a remarkable record of rapid development with a minimum of inflation. The agricultural sector has played an important role in achieving this development and could play an even more important role in the future.

Publication of this book is partially funded under the AID/211(d) grant to Iowa State University. Its contents may be quoted freely and without permission. The authors assume sole responsibility for its content and conclusions. The views and opinions expressed in the book do not necessarily represent those of any particular institute, agency, or individual.

WILLIAM C. MERRILL
LEHMAN B. FLETCHER
RANDALL A. HOFFMANN
MICHAEL J. APPLEGATE

PANAMA'S ECONOMIC DEVELOPMENT: THE ROLE OF AGRICULTURE

CHAPTER ONE

ECONOMIC GROWTH AND PERFORMANCE

PANAMA'S GEOGRAPHIC LOCATION at the crossroads between the Atlantic and Pacific oceans and the North and South American continents has had considerable influence on the nature of the country's economic development. Trade and communication routes across the isthmus have existed since the Spanish Conquest. Transshipment of merchandise and passengers flourished following construction of a railway across the isthmus in the 1850s. Completion of the Panama Canal in 1914 confirmed the critical role of trade and service in the economy; the economy has retained its externally oriented, service-centered character.

Historically, employment and income generated by the canal have been major factors in economic growth. In the 1960s, however, economic dependence on the canal was lessened by rapid development of non-Zone commercial and financial activities and by increasing exports of bananas, petroleum products, shrimp, and sugar. Economic diversification is expected to continue.

Panama has a land area of 29,000 square miles and a population (1970) of 1.4 million. Population growth accelerated after 1950, averaging about 3.1% per year in the 1960s. This high rate of population growth has resulted in a marked reduction in the average age and an increase in the number of dependents per economically active person. It also has led to a rapid rise in the number of workers in the labor force. The number of economically active persons 15 years old and older increased from 330,000 in 1960 to 466,000 in 1970. The population growth rate is expected to remain at 3% per year for the foreseeable future.

ECONOMIC GROWTH SINCE 1950

Gross domestic product (GDP) in real terms (expressed in 1960 balboas) grew from B/259.2 million in 1950 to B/971.6 million in 1971 (1 balboa equals U.S. $1) (Table 1.1.). The average annual rate of

TABLE 1.1. • **GROSS DOMESTIC PRODUCT AT MARKET PRICES, 1950–71 (MILLIONS OF 1960 BALBOAS)**

Year	GDP	Year	GDP
1950	259.2	1961	460.9
1951	256.9	1962	498.9
1952	270.7	1963	541.5
1953	287.2	1964	565.5
1954	297.5	1965	617.3
1955	314.7	1966	664.1
1956	331.1	1967	720.9
1957	365.7	1968	771.2
1958	368.6	1969	836.3
1959	392.2	1970	894.5
1960	415.8	1971	971.6[a]

Source: Dirección de Estadística y Censo.

[a]Preliminary.

growth for the 1950–71 period was 6.5%. During the 1960s, however, the average annual rate of growth of GDP exceeded 8% per year. Unquestionably, the country has entered the 1970s following a decade of sustained growth at a high level.

The growth rate of the economy demonstrated more stability in the 1960s than in the 1950s. During the fifties, annual growth fluctuated from less than 1% to more than 10%. Since 1960, however, the growth rate has fallen below 7% in only one year. Growth has been equally vigorous in per capita terms. Real GDP per person rose from B/392 in 1960 to B/657 in 1971. The average annual increase in per capita output during 1960–71 was 4.8%. This level is considerably above the target rate set by the Alliance for Progress and is one of the highest in Latin America. Moreover, until recently, the high rate of growth has largely been achieved with minimal inflation. The overall price level, as measured by the implicit deflator for GDP, rose only 13% during the 1960–69 period. In 1970, however, the implicit GDP inflator jumped to 117, and preliminary data for 1971 indicate a further increase to about 120.

The macroeconomic sources of the impressive growth performance of the economy are not difficult to detect. Gross investment in 1960 balboas increased from B/67.8 million in 1960 to B/276.5 million in 1971. As a proportion of GDP, gross investment increased from a range of 16% to 20% in 1960–65 to 22%–29% in 1966–71. Gross investment equaled 27.1% of GDP in 1970 and 28.5% in 1971. In other terms, the economy currently is devoting a fourth or more of its output each year to investment for renewal and enlargement of its capital stock.

While both private and public investment have been growing, public investment now accounts for a larger share of the total than in the early 1960s. In 1966–71, public investment averaged about 18% to 22% of total investment, up from 13% to 15% in 1960–65. Nevertheless, private investment at a level of 20% or more of GDP has been one of the strongest factors in the growth performance of the economy.

Consumption claims against domestic ouput grew (in real terms) at an average annual rate of 7% over the 1960–71 period, less than the rate of growth of GDP. As a result, the average propensity to consume in the private and public sectors has fallen consistently in the 1960s. This reduction has permitted the growth of domestic savings.

The export sector also performed extremely well during the 1960s. Bananas accounted for a major part of growth in earnings from exports of goods. The banana industry generates slightly over half of total exports of goods and is a key factor in the performance of the external sector. Increased exports of refined petroleum products, shrimp, and sugar also occurred. Another important element in the external sector's development has been the increase in earnings of Panamanians working in the Canal Zone. Much of this increase originated in the Canal Company's decision to increase all wages to the U.S. minimum. This adjustment, which is essentially complete, has resulted in earnings for Panamanian workers in the Zone that are well above wages for comparable workers in the national labor market.

In summary, Panama achieved substantial real growth without significant inflation during the decade of the sixties. The growth process proceeded in classic fashion. Domestic savings rose to sustain growth in investment, and a dynamic external sector generated foreign exchange for capital imports without severely squeezing imports for consumption. The sources of the high rate of growth will be quantified later in this chapter. Quantitative analysis of the macroeconomic structure of the economy and the implications of a continued high rate of growth for the agricultural sector will be presented in Chapter 2.

SECTORAL COMPOSITION OF THE ECONOMY

Important changes have taken place since 1950 in the sectoral composition of output and employment. The process of structural transformation is described in this section. Total GDP can be divided into ten production sectors. The three-year average percentage composition of GDP by sector of origin is given in Table 1.2 for 1950–52, 1959–61, and 1969–71. Three-year averages are used because they are influenced less by year-to-year variations in sectoral output and hence reflect more clearly the underlying long-term growth processes at work in the economy. The table also shows the number of workers employed and output per worker in each sector for 1960 and 1970.

In terms of share of GDP, the agricultural sector (including forestry and fishing) is the largest production sector and accounted for 18.2% of real GDP in 1969–71, compared to 27.2% in 1950–52. Since 1950–52, the agricultural sector has grown at an average rate of 4.32% per year. The growth rate of agricultural output was somewhat higher in the sixties (5.06%) than in the fifties (3.82%).

Within the agricultural sector, export crop production (bananas, sugar) has been the most dynamic subsector, increasing by more than 9% annually during the 1960s. In contrast, crops for internal consumption increased at an average annual rate of only 4%. Indeed, during 1966–71, domestic food production increased at only 2.5% annually, less than the rate of population growth. The slow growth rate of domestic food production has been reflected in higher food prices, an indicator of agricultural performance that will be discussed later in this section.

The second most important production sector in 1969–71 was manufacturing, which contributed 17.4% of total GDP. The share of manufacturing in GDP has risen steadily since 1950–52. Growth in manufacturing output has consistently been above the overall growth rate, averaging about 10% per year during the two decades. The government has provided tariff and quota protection and tax incentives to promote industrial development. Industrial production for the national market has increased, but little progress has been made in developing industrial production for export.

The service sector was the third largest component of GDP in 1969–71 (16.2%). This sector, like agriculture, has declined as a proportion of total output in the economy. Trade is the only other sector that accounts for more than 10% of total output. Since 1950, wholesale and retail commerce have maintained an almost constant share of GDP, slightly less than 14%.

Construction, transportation, and housing each accounted for between 6% and 7% of GDP in 1969–71. The share of both construction and transportation has been increasing, while the housing sector share of GDP has been decreasing. Goods and services supplied to the Canal Zone represented slightly more than 8% of GDP in 1969–71. This proportion was up from 7.1% in 1959–61. Thus, during the 1960s, the Canal Zone component of GDP grew somewhat more rapidly (9.06%) than total output. Finance and utilities, although small as a proportion of total output (3.8% and 2.9% in 1969–71, respectively), were the fastest growing areas of the economy during the 1960s.

In total, the economy presents an output structure that is quite different from a typical less developed economy. Agricultural output has declined to less than 20% of total GDP. Contributions of both the manufacturing and service sectors are similar in size to those of agriculture. Manufacturing is the largest economic sector that has consistently grown at a rate faster than the total economy. The service sector has declined along with the agricultural sector. Construction, transportation, finance, and utilities are the other sectors whose growth has led the overall economy.

Total employment rose from 300,000 in 1960 to 433,000 in 1970, an increase over the entire period of almost 50%, or an average annual increase of almost 4%. (These data pertain to the labor force defined to include persons 15 years old or older.) The increase in jobs compares favorably to the overall growth performance of the economy.

More workers are employed in the agricultural sector than in any other. Nevertheless, the share of the labor force working in agriculture has declined substantially from 50% in 1960 to 36.5% of total employment in 1970. The number of farm workers rose only slightly from 150,000 in 1960 to 158,000 in 1970. This change corresponds to an average annual increase of only 0.5%. The service sector is the second largest employer of labor. Service workers represented 24.2% of the work force in 1970, up from 19.7% in 1960. Employment in services rose from 59,000 in 1960 to 105,000 in 1970.

Manufacturing and trade each accounted for 11% of employment in 1970. Both have increased their share of workers since 1960. Employment increased at an average rate of 8.11% in manufacturing and 6.54% in trade in the 1960s. Employment grew faster in utilities, finance, and construction than in the other sectors. By 1970, construction accounted for 5.5% of the work force, while finance and utilities accounted for 1.6% and 0.9%, respectively. Employment of Panamanians in the Canal Zone increased by 2% annually during the 1960–70 period. Five percent of Panama's labor force worked in the Zone in 1970.

Gross domestic product per worker in each of the sectors is presented in the right-hand columns of Table 1.2. The three largest sectors of the economy present interesting contrasts. Gross domestic product per worker was lowest in agriculture but nevertheless increased from B/638 to B/1,020, or at an average rate of 4.81% annually between 1960 and 1970. While the growth rate of total agricultural output was below the national average, the growth rate of output per worker in agriculture was greater than those of all other sectors except the Canal Zone and transportation. Total industrial output, in contrast, grew rapidly, but output per worker in manufacturing rose only 2.46% per year, reflecting the rapid growth of employment in manufacturing. Out-

TABLE 1.2. • SECTORAL COMPOSITION OF OUTPUT AND EMPLOYMENT

Sector	GDP by Sector (%)			Growth in Output		
	1950-52	1959-61	1969-71	1950-52 to 1959-61	1959-61 to 1969-71	1950-52 to 1969-71
Agriculture[a]	27.2	23.7	18.2	3.82	5.06	4.32
Manufacturing[b]	10.3	13.4	17.4	8.57	10.73	9.69
Construction	4.2	5.4	6.1	8.52	9.10	8.84
Trade	13.7	13.5	13.9	5.35	8.17	6.84
Transportation[c]	3.9	4.7	6.6	7.80	11.50	9.73
Finance[d]	1.9	2.5	3.8	8.40	13.15	10.69
Services[e]	20.6	19.6	16.2	4.87	5.88	5.40
Utilities[f]	1.3	1.9	2.9	9.91	12.62	11.38
Housing	9.1	8.2	6.7	4.08	5.79	5.00
Canal Zone	7.8	7.1	8.2	3.13	9.06	6.79
Total	100.0	100.0	100.0	5.45	7.85	6.71

TABLE 1.2. • (CONTINUED)

Sector	Employment by Sector					GDP per Worker Employed		
	1960		1970		Growth per year 1960-70 (%)	1960 (1960 balboas)	1970	Growth per year 1960-70 (%)
	No. (000)	%	No. (000)	%				
Agriculture[a]	150	50.0	158	36.5	0.52	638	1,020	4.81
Manufacturing[b]	22	7.3	48	11.1	8.11	2,527	3,248	2.46
Construction	10	3.3	24	5.5	9.15	2,290	2,250	-0.17
Trade	26	8.7	49	11.3	6.54	2,227	2,584	1.50
Transportation[c]	9	3.0	16	3.7	5.92	2,144	3,725	5.68
Finance[d]	3	1.0	7	1.6	8.84	3,433	4,971	3.77
Services[e]	59	19.7	105	24.2	5.94	1,369	1,391	0.16
Utilities[f]	1	0.3	4	0.9	14.87	8,400	6,500	-2.06
Housing	--	--	--	--	--	--	--	--
Canal Zone	18	6.0	22	5.1	2.03	1,689	3,195	6.58
Total	300	99.3[g]	433	99.8[g]	3.74	1,386	2,066	4.07

Source: Calculated from data obtained from Dirección de Estadística y Censo.

[a]Includes crops, livestock, forestry, and fishing.
[b]Includes mining.
[c]Includes storage and communication.
[d]Includes banking, insurance, real estate, and other financial activity.
[e]Includes public and private services and public administration.
[f]Includes electricity, gas, water, and sewage.
[g]Not equal to 100% due to rounding.

put and employment in services grew at almost the same rate, with the result that output per worker in services changed very little. Output per worker fell slightly in the construction sector. The Canal Zone had the most rapid growth in output per worker. The data in Table 1.2 show that real earnings per worker in the Zone increased an average of 6.58% per year during 1960–70.

The structural transformation of the economy is proceeding rapidly. Rural-urban migration kept the growth in the agricultural labor force to less than 1% per year during the 1960s. If this trend continues, the farm work force should reach its maximum in the late 1970s and begin to decline in absolute terms. Some additional labor has been absorbed in manufacturing, transportation, and finance as well as in the Canal Zone where output per worker is high. However, much of the additional urban employment has been in services, where output per worker is only slightly higher than in agriculture. The importance of shifts in the rural-urban composition of the work force as a factor explaining the growth of the economy will be evaluated.

The implicit price index for GDP in the agricultural sector was 124 in 1970 (1960 = 100) compared to 108 for the industrial sector. This comparison suggests that the agricultural sector was responsible for a significant part of the inflationary pressures in Panama in the late 1960s. This conclusion is supported by movements in market price indexes. The consumer price index for low-income and moderate-income families in Panama City was 116 in 1970 and 114 in 1971 (1962 = 100). The index for the food component, however, was 116 in 1970 and 119 in 1971. The index increased by 5% during the first six months of 1972, an unusually high increase and a clear reflection of more intense inflationary pressures.

In a market economy, relative price changes signal the need for resource reallocation in response to demand and supply changes. Rising prices in the absence of sufficient supply response can touch off an inflationary process leading to upward movements in the general price level. Rising food prices, for example, increase the cost of living and induce workers in urban occupations to demand higher wage and salary increases. If wage increases in excess of productivity gains are granted, costs of production rise, compelling producers to raise prices to protect profit margins. In this manner, general inflation can follow from the failure of output in one sector to respond to price signals. The relative rise in domestic food prices, therefore, indicates a failure of the agricultural sector to respond to price signals and poses a threat to overall price stability. Policies to promote output growth are indicated but should be formulated on the basis of more detailed analysis of demand and supply balances for each of the major food items. Projections for the major food products are contained in Chapter 4.

TABLE 1.3. • SOURCES OF PAST GROWTH

Factor	Contribution to Growth of GDP (%)
Increased Employment of Labor	2.6
Increase in Capital Stock	2.0
Education and Migration	1.5
Canal Zone Wage Increases	0.7
Residual Factors	1.2
Total	8.0

Source: Harberger, 1972, p. 27.

SOURCES OF GROWTH AND FUTURE PROSPECTS

Studies have been made to attempt to identify the quantitative contributions that various factors have made to the overall growth rate of the economy.[1] These studies have emphasized factors whose contribution to growth can be evaluated quantitatively and also have identified other factors whose influence is not directly quantifiable. The contribution of the latter group of growth factors was measured as a residual; i.e., they were taken to explain the amount of observed growth that remained after the effects of the quantifiable factors were removed.

The breakdown of the observed 8% growth rate arrived at in these studies is given in Table 1.3. The quantifiable factors, discussed individually below, appear to have contributed 6.8 percentage points of growth per year, a very large share of total growth. Residual factors such as the forces of technical change and increased efficiency in resource use account for the remaining 1.2 percentage points. This contribution of residual elements can be considered to be quite small on the basis of experience in other countries. If these estimates are accepted as reasonable, Panama's growth in the 1960s, although at an exceedingly high rate, was a growth whose sources can be identified and in large measure quantified.

---

1. This section is based on L. A. Sjaastad, Prospects for Economic Growth in the 1970's, GOP report, March 1972; and A. C. Harberger, The Past Growth and Future Prospects of the Panamanian Economy, GOP report, June 1972.

The growth of employment, at a rate above 4% per year, was itself the result of three separate influences: (1) the population component (15 years and over) from which the labor force is drawn grew at a rate of some 3% per year; (2) the fraction of that population component classified as economically active (i.e., in the labor force) grew at about 1% per year; and (3) the fraction of the labor force that was actually employed increased at an average rate of about 0.35% per year. The combination of these influences led to an increase in the actual number of people employed at an average rate of 4.35% per year. If share of labor in the GDP is taken to be approximately 60%, an increase of 2.6 (0.60 × 4.35) percentage points of annual GDP growth can be attributed to the simple increase in numbers of workers employed, taking their average quality to be constant.

The growth in capital stock was accomplished by a rate of gross investment that averaged at least 20% of GDP. Of course, a part of gross investment of any year simply serves to offset the gradual deterioration and retirement of the existing capital stock. The national accounts assume that this fraction is around 50% of gross investment, equal to some 10% of GDP. If one takes gross investment averaging 20% of GDP and subtracts capital consumption allowances (depreciation) averaging 10%, the result is an average net investment also equal to 10% of GDP. The contribution of increased capital to the growth of GDP is measured by the rate of net investment (here 10%) times the estimated rate of productivity of capital. For purposes of measuring the impact of investment on the growth rate of GDP, the rate of productivity of capital should be measured gross of taxes and gross of depreciation. If the gross-of-tax, gross-of-depreciation rate of return to capital is taken to be 20% in real terms, capital's contribution to the growth rate of GDP is 2.0 (10.0 × 0.20) percentage points per year.

The combined influence of education and migration on the growth of GDP is calculated in Table 1.4. Column (1) presents the distribution of urban and rural members of the male labor force in 1960, while column (2) shows how the 1970 male labor force would have looked had there been no change in the urban-rural location, or in the educational level between 1960 and 1970. The combined influence of education and migration is found by multiplying each item in column (2) by 410/230, the ratio of the size of the male labor force in 1970 to that of 1960, so that the grand total of column (2) is the same as that of column (3), which shows the actual distribution of the male labor force in 1970.

Comparison of urban and rural totals of columns (2) and (3) shows the degree of labor force migration that took place above and beyond that which would compensate for differential rates of natural increase of the urban and rural labor force over the decade. According to these calculations, there were 57,000 more workers in the urban area and 57,000 less in the rural area in 1970 than there would have been without

TABLE 1.4. • EFFECTS OF EDUCATION AND MIGRATION, 1960–70, MALE LABOR FORCE

Years of Education & Location	(1) Male Labor Force, 1960[a] (000)	(2) Male Labor Force, 1970, Distributed as in (1) [Col.(1)[b] x 410/230] (000)	(3) Male Labor Force, 1970, Actual Distribution[c] (000)	(4) Assumed Earnings Pattern (index)	(5) Total Earnings Index, Labor Distribution as in (2) [(2) x (4)]	(6) Total Earnings Index, Labor Distribution as in (3) [(3) x (4)]
			Urban			
0 – 5	38	67	71	2.0	134	142
6	12	22	53	3.0	66	159
7 – 11	23	41	54	4.0	164	216
12	5	9	15	8.0	72	120
13 – 17	5	9	10	24.0	216	240
18+	1	2	4	40.0	80	160
Total Urban	84	150	207	- -	732	1,037
			Rural			
0 – 5	126	224	140	1.0	224	140
6	15	27	41	1.5	41	61
7 – 11	4	7	15	2.0	14	30
12	1	2	4	4.0	8	16
13 – 17	- -	- -	2	12.0	- -	24
18+	- -	- -	1	20.0	- -	20
Total Rural	146	260	203	- -	287	291
Grand Total	230	410	410	- -	1,019	1,328

Source: Harberger, 1972, p. 27.

[a]Census of Population, 1970, Vol. V, Table 134. The classification by years of education in the 1960 census was different from that used in the 1970 census. To make them comparable, the 1960 data were interpolated to adjust the 1960 classification to the same basis as the 1970 data.

[b]This represents a proportional upward adjustment of column (1), to reflect the growth of the total labor force between 1960 and 1970.

[c]Census of Population, 1970, Table 6.

migration between 1960 and 1970. Comparison of the separate urban and rural totals of columns (2) and (3) illustrates the migration effect. Clearly, the difference between these totals is also reflected in the separate cells (classified by levels of education) of the urban and rural sections of the table for the two years. Therefore, the table shows the combined effect of changes in both educational and locational patterns.

Column (4) contains assumptions about average earnings per worker by level of education and rural and urban locations. For both urban and rural workers, for example, those with 12 years of education were assumed to have four times the average earnings of those with 0–5 years of schooling. Similarly, those with 13–17 years of education were assumed to have average earnings equal to 12 times those of the 0–5 years of education bracket. Comparing urban and rural locations, workers in a given educational bracket were assumed to earn on the average twice as much if they worked in urban areas as they would if employed in the rural sector. This is not to say that they were twice as well off as a consequence of working in urban areas since significant differences exist in the cost of living between the two sectors. However, the fact remains that when workers move from rural to urban employment, their wages typically increase substantially on the average, thus contributing to a rise in the measured GDP.

These figures are not based directly on Panamanian data, but they are considered to reflect the pattern of educational and urban-rural differentials that typically prevail in countries at or near Panama's stage of development. They are very close to the differentials used in Sjaastad's 1972 study, which in turn were derived from Chilean data for 1964.

Columns (5) and (6) are obtained by multiplying the number of workers in each cell of columns (2) and (3), respectively, by the index of relative wage level given in the corresponding cell of column (4). The result is an index of total earnings by workers of each education-location characteristic, either what they would have been in the absence of changes in the education-location pattern since 1960 [column (5)] or what they actually were in 1970 [column (6)].

Since columns (5) and (6) would be exactly the same if there had been no change in the education-location pattern since 1960, the difference of 31% between their two grand totals represents the combined effects on labor earnings of migration and of changes in composition of the labor force by level of education for the ten-year period. This increase amounts to an annual average increment of 2.5% in the earnings of labor due to changes in the education-location mix. Applying this percentage of increase to labor's share in the GDP gives 1.5 (2.5×0.60) as the corresponding contribution of this factor to the GDP growth rate. This result is not very sensitive to the assumed premium of the earnings of urban workers over those of their rural counterparts in each educational bracket. If this premium were zero; i.e., if urban workers earned just the same as rural workers of the same educational characteristics instead of double the rural wage, the urban total of column (5) would be 366 and that of column (6) would be 518. The grand totals of (5) and (6) would then be 653 and 809, respectively, and the ratio between the two would be 1.24 instead of 1.31. If there were, in fact, no premium, the estimate would be that changes in the education-location mix would have raised labor earnings by 2.0% rather than 2.5% per year and would have contributed 1.2 (2.0 × 0.60) rather than 1.5 percentage points to the growth rate of GDP. The difference in the estimated contribution is obviously quite minor in comparison with the drastically different assumptions made concerning the size of the premium earned by urban workers.

The rise of Canal Zone wages also contributed to Panama's growth rate during the 1960s. Average monthly wages rose from B/175 to B/379 between 1960 and 1969. During the same period, the consumer price index rose from 100 to 108.6, so that in terms of 1960 balboas, the average monthly salary rose from B/175 to B/349, or by almost precisely 100%. The contribution to total growth from this source was, therefore, B/174 × 12 × 16,369, where the last figure represents the number of non-U.S. workers in the Canal Zone in 1969. This calculation amounts to some B/34 million for 1960–70, which equals about 6% of the average GDP for the period. Expressed on an annual basis, the contribution of this component to the annual growth rate was about 0.7 percentage points.

The increase in the employed labor force will continue to be an important source of growth in the future, though not as important as in the past. The reason for its decreasing importance is that the 1960s were characterized by a significant rise in labor force participation; since the participation rate is already quite high (58.2% of those over 15 years of age were in the labor force in 1970), it is unlikely that any further substantial increase will occur. The projected participation rate for 1980 is only slightly higher (59.0%) than that of 1970. This projection forecasts a labor force growth of slightly less than 3.5% per year. Allowing for continued improvement in the employment rate as well, the overall increase in the employed labor force is anticipated to average 3.8% per year over the 1970–80 decade. This percentage, applied to labor's estimated share in GDP of 60%, yields an expected contribution to growth of 2.3% from increased employment of labor, compared to the higher estimated contribution of 2.6% over the decade of the 1960s.

The growth of the stock of capital, in contrast to that of the labor force, has the potential to be greater in the 1970s than it was in the 1960s. While the rate of gross investment averaged 20% over the 1960s, it exhibited a rising trend, reaching levels in excess of 25% in the

TABLE 1.5. ● EFFECTS OF EDUCATION AND MIGRATION, 1970–80, MALE LABOR FORCE

Years of Education & Location	(1) Male Labor Force, 1970[a] (000)	(2) Male Labor Force, 1980, Distributed as in (1)[b] (000)	(3) Male Labor Force, 1980, Projected Actual Distribution[c] (000)	(4) Assumed Earnings Pattern[d] (index)	(5) Total Earnings Index, Labor Distribution as in (2) [(2) x (4)]	(6) Total Earnings Index, Labor Distribution as in (3) [(3) x (4)]
Urban						
0 - 5	71	98	95	2.0	196	190
6	53	73	86	3.0	219	258
7 - 11	54	74	93	4.0	296	372
12	15	21	29	8.0	168	232
13 - 17	10	14	19	24.0	336	454
18+	4	6	7	40.0	240	280
Total Urban	207	286	329	--	1,455	1,786
Rural						
0 - 5	140	195	151	1.0	195	151
6	41	57	51	1.5	86	76
7 - 11	15	21	25	2.0	42	50
12	4	5	8	4.0	20	32
13 - 17	2	3	3	12.0	36	36
18+	1	1	1	20.0	20	20
Total Rural	203	282	239	--	399	365
Total Male	410	568	568	--	1,854	2,151

Source: Harberger, 1972, pp. 32–38.

[a] Sjaastad, 1972, Table A5.

[b] Column (1) x (568/410).

[c] Sjaastad, 1972.

[d] The same earnings pattern was assumed for the different educational levels of the male labor force as was used in constructing Table 1.4.

early 1970s. This rate is high compared to those of most other countries. How reasonable is it to believe that this high rate of investment can be maintained in the future? If it is, the contribution of capital to the growth rate (estimated at 2.0 percentage points per year for the 1960s) can be expected to be 2.5 percentage points per year for the 1970s.

The combined effect of education and migration is projected to be somewhat lower in the 1970s than it was in the 1960s. Table 1.5 and Table 1.6 present the relevant data, the 1970 labor force figures are based on census data, and the projections for 1980 are taken from Sjaastad's study.[2] In this case, data are available on female workers as well as the male labor force. Data on female workers are presented in Table 1.6. The methodology underlying the construction of these tables is the same as that used to develop Table 1.4. However, inclusion of the female labor force in the calculations necessitated assuming a relative earning pattern for this group. Wages of male workers of a given educational category were assumed to differ from those of female workers by a factor of 2.0. Thus the pattern reflected in column (4) of Table 1.6 represents exactly half (for each education-location category) of the corresponding number in column (4) of Table 1.5.

In regard to the projected contribution to the GDP growth rate of changes in the education-location mix of the labor force, the relevant data are the grand totals at the bottom of columns (5) and (6) of Table 1.6. These figures indicate that labor earnings in 1980 are projected to be 17% higher (3,169 compared with 2,709) than they would be in the absence of changes in labor force composition with respect to education and location. On an annual basis, this increase represents a contribution of some 1.4 percentage points to the growth of labor earnings and of some 0.84 (1.4 $\times$ 0.60) percentage points to the growth rate of GDP. These calculations assume that an additional 43,000 male workers will migrate from rural to urban locations between 1970 and 1980, compared to the 57,000 that migrated between 1960 and 1970. The female labor force analysis projects a migration of 38,000 in the 1970s. The contribution to growth in the 1970s from the education-migration factor is expected to be lower than in the 1960s, primarily because rural-urban migrants will make up a smaller proportion of the urban work force.

Canal Zone wage increases in the 1970s are not likely to be as dramatic as those of the 1960s when wages were brought up to the standard dictated by U.S. minimum wage legislation. It is possible, however, that during 1970–80 a revised agreement between the governments of Panama and the United States could result in canal revenue increases that would tend to offset the reduction in the contribution of actual Canal Zone wage increases to Panama's rate of economic growth.

---

2. Sjaastad, 1972.

TABLE 1.6. ● **EFFECTS OF EDUCATION AND MIGRATION, 1970–80, FEMALE LABOR FORCE**

Years of Education & Location	(1) Female Labor Force, 1970[a] (000)	(2) Female Labor Force, 1980, Distributed as in (1)[b] (000)	(3) Female Labor Force, 1980, Projected Actual Distribution[c] (000)	(4) Assumed Earnings Pattern (index)	(5) Total Earnings Index, Labor Distribution as in (2) [(2) × (4)]	(6) Total Earnings Index, Labor Distribution as in (3) [(3) × (4)]
			Urban			
0 – 5	78	110	104	1.0	110	104
6	59	83	92	1.5	125	148
7 – 11	54	76	96	2.0	152	192
12	16	22	32	4.0	88	128
13 – 17	9	13	17	12.0	156	194
18+	2	3	4	20.0	60	80
Total Urban	218	307	345	– –	691	846
			Rural			
0 – 5	124	174	132	0.5	87	66
6	34	48	43	0.7	36	33
7 – 11	15	21	23	1.0	21	23
12	5	7	11	2.0	14	22
13 – 17	1	1	3	6.0	6	18
18+	– –	– –	1	10.0	– –	10
Total Rural	179	251	213	– –	164	172
Total Female	397	558	558	– –	855	1,018
Grand Total (Male plus Female)					2,709	3,169

Source: Harberger, 1972, pp. 32–38.

[a]Sjaastad, 1972, Table AS.

[b]Column (1) × (558/397).

[c]Sjaastad, 1972.

TABLE 1.7. • PROJECTED SOURCES OF GROWTH

Source of Growth	Contribution to Growth of GDP (%)
Increased Employment of Labor	2.3
Growth in the Stock of Capital	2.5
Education and Migration	0.8
Residual Factors	1.2
Total	6.8

Source: Harberger, 1972, p. 35.

Future growth prospects are summarized in Table 1.7. If residual factors were to operate with at least comparable force (1.2 percentage points per year) in the 1970s as in the 1960s, the projected growth rate would rise to 6.8% per year, without counting any contribution from increases in Canal Zone wages or from new arrangements regarding canal revenues. Although forecasts for the canal factor are highly uncertain, a projection of continued growth at 8% per year in real terms appears to be within the range of possibility for Panama in the 1970s.

Nevertheless, continued growth at the high rate of 8% per year cannot be simply assumed as a certainty. One prerequisite is that exports increase as rapidly in the future as they have in the past. The macroeconomic model presented in Chapter 2 quantifies the importance of the external sector and shows the impact of alternative levels of exports on the forecasted growth rate of the economy. The rate of investment is another key growth factor. If it is not possible to maintain the high rate of investment achieved in the 1960s, not only will the direct contribution of capital to growth in output fall but employment and migration factors will contribute less to growth as well. Thus a fall in private investment to, say, 15% of GDP could lead to a rate of growth as low as 5% to 6% per year.

It seems likely that the natural increase in the urban labor force will be sufficient in the future to fill the high-wage jobs that will be created in manufacturing, finance, and utilities. In the 1970s, unskilled, rural migrants are likely to find, even more than in past years, that low-

TABLE 1.8. ● NATIONAL PER CAPITA INCOME, 1960–70

Year	Income per Capita (1960 balboas)
1960	319
1961	346
1962	365
1963	398
1964	419
1965	437
1966	463
1967	496
1968	515
1969	548
1970	586

Source: Dirección de Estadística y Censo, Ingreso Nacional, Años 1969 y 1970, p. 11.

income service and trade occupations offer their only point of entry into the urban work force. This situation has important implications for the type of training that should be provided for potential migrants.

INCOME DISTRIBUTION

Average income has risen consistently since 1960 (Table 1.8). The average income for 1970 was B/586 per person, which is high compared to other Latin American countries. If the future growth rate equals that of the past, Panama will soon have a per capita income in Latin America second only to Venezuela. But what about the distribution of this income? Does the familiar dual economy exist below the surface of this scintillating growth in GDP? What part of the population shares in the larger output? Does growth benefit the rich proportionately more than the poor? Is a considerable part of the population bypassed by economic growth, increasing the inequity of income distribution? Answers to these questions are important in establishing priority goals and objectives for agricultural development.

A comprehensive study of income distribution has been completed by McClure using 1969 data.[3] A subsequent study revised the estimates, using 1970 data, and extended them to the province levels.[4] Although made with care, these studies rest on inadequate and imperfect data. Nevertheless, if interpreted with caution, they give at least a rough indication of the pattern of income distribution that existed in 1969–70 at the end of a decade of vigorous growth.

McClure's overall results are shown in Table 1.9. The poorest half of income recipients apparently received about 15% of income in 1969, while the top 10% received about 45% of income. The inequality in Panama is slightly less than in Colombia; about equal to Mexico, Guatemala, and Venezuela; and somewhat higher than Ecuador, Argentina, and Chile.[5] This conclusion may surprise many observers, considering apparently broad-based advances in industry, finance, and commerce and signs of a growing and prosperous middle class. Yet several reasons explain why the degree of inequality of income distribution remains high.

First, a considerable portion of the economically active population is engaged in low-income occupations. In the urban sector, the lowest income recipients are those working in domestic and other service activities and small-scale retailing. In the rural sector, operators of small, largely subsistence farms are the low-income recipients. These groups comprise most of the 27% that received incomes of less than B/500 per year. Almost half of all income recipients received less than B/1,000 per year. This half of the work force has benefited little from economic growth. Their incomes may be somewhat higher than corresponding groups in other developing countries, but they remain mired in poverty in relation to those of the work force at more privileged middle and upper income levels.

One might surmise that employment of a large part of the labor force in the Canal Zone and in manufacturing, government, financial, and commercial activities in Panama City and Colon would moderate inequality in income distribution. But the effect of this employment cannot be demonstrated. Instead, relatively well-paid workers in the Canal Zone, government, commerce, finance, and industry fall toward the top of the income distribution pyramid. For example, about 40% of Canal Zone employees fall in the top 10% of income recipients.[6]

3. C. E. McClure, Jr., The Distribution of Income and Tax Incidence in Panama, 1969, GOP report, n.d.
4. G. S. Sahota, Public Expenditure and Income Distribution in Panama, GOP report, August 1972.
5. McClure, p. 41.
6. McClure, p. 42.

TABLE 1.9. ● DISTRIBUTION OF INCOME, 1969

Income Bracket (balboas)	Number of Persons (000) (a)	Total Income (B/000,000) (b)	Percentage of Total Persons (c)	Income (d)	Cumulative Percentage of Total Persons (e)	Income (f)
0 - 500	86.5	27.0	23.0	3.7	23.0	3.7
500 - 1,000	84.6	63.5	22.5	8.6	45.6	12.3
1,000 - 1,500	72.3	97.2	19.3	13.2	64.8	25.5
1,500 - 2,000	48.6	92.4	12.9	12.5	77.8	38.0
2,000 - 2,500	25.6	63.1	6.8	8.6	84.6	46.6
2,500 - 3,600	24.2	81.0	6.4	11.0	91.0	57.6
3,600 - 6,000	20.3	106.0	5.4	14.4	96.4	71.9
6,000 - 10,000	8.4	73.0	2.2	9.9	98.7	81.8
10,000 - 20,000	3.2	55.0	0.9	7.5	99.5	89.3
20,000 - 50,000	1.2	39.8	0.3	5.4	99.8	94.7
Over 50,000	0.7	39.0	0.2	5.3	100.0	100.0
Total	375.5	737.0	100.0	100.0	100.0	--

Source: McClure, p. 39. The data in the table correspond to McClure's "estimate B" which contains an optimistic treatment of the operators of small farms.

Thus a development pattern apparently promoting equality, in fact, conceals an essentially dual economy where small farmers, retailers, and service workers would seem to have little hope of escaping poverty.

Another factor explaining the quite unequal distribution of income must surely be the market power position enjoyed by domestic producers in many industries. The national market is so small that in many industries it can be supplied by only one or two firms operating at efficient levels. The government has followed an import substitution policy to promote industrial development, using tariffs and quotas on imports to protect domestic producers from foreign competition. The result of this policy has been that consumers of these products have subsidized a small number of industrial producers and their work forces by paying prices much in excess of import price levels. To the extent that import substitution development in industry has led to high-cost production, the low-income half of the population is forced to pay high prices for many objects of common consumption.

An important characteristic of these estimates of income distribution should be noted. Most estimates of the size distribution of income relate to the way income is distributed among families. Since no data on family incomes are available, the size distribution of income among economically active individuals was estimated. The one exception was that unpaid family employees were added together with the heads of their households. In agriculture, therefore, where there was one unpaid family employee for every two self-employed persons, the income data are more nearly on a family basis, resulting in some understatement of the relative economic positions of farm families.

Income distribution by province and sector was estimated for 1970 by Sahota.[7] His estimates of average per capita incomes by province and sector are given in Table 1.10. The location of the provinces is shown in Figure 1.1. In most official documents of the country the San Blas territory is treated for statistical purposes as a part of Colon province. On a national basis, urban income per capita is almost three times as high as rural income per capita. Province averages vary by a factor of 6 from B/881 for Panama to B/145 for Darien. Per capita income of Panama province is almost identical with the overall urban per capita income. Income inequality was found to be highest in Los Santos, Veraguas, Cocle, and Chiriqui provinces. Panama province ranked about in the middle in terms of relative inequality. The relatively egalitarian provinces were Colon and Bocas del Toro.

Sahota also found that income distribution in the rural sector is significantly more unequal (with a Gini coefficient of 0.689) than in the urban sector (with a Gini coefficient of 0.521). Rural income is both much lower and more unequally distributed than urban income. The causes of this relative poverty and unequal income distribution in the agricultural sector should be identified and possible remedies given high priority in agricultural development planning for Panama.

IMPLICATIONS FOR AGRICULTURAL DEVELOPMENT

All societies, whatever their form of economic organization, have a number of economic and social goals. National goals frequently in-

7. Sahota, 1972, pp. 12–28.

TABLE 1.10. • PER CAPITA INCOMES BY PROVINCE AND SECTOR, 1970 (BALBOAS)

Province	Urban	Rural	Total
Bocas del Toro	614	289	402
Cocle	544	225	295
Colon	771	821	794
Chiriqui	553	310	373
Darien	364	92	145
Herrera	495	230	314
Los Santos	556	246	290
Panama	1,015	367	881
Veraguas	511	170	212
National	874	319	583

Source: Based on Sahota, 1972, Appendix Tables D4.1 and D4.2.

clude (1) economic growth leading to increases in per capita income, (2) price stability, (3) full and efficient utilization of resources, and (4) an equitable distribution of income and wealth. Evidence reviewed in this chapter suggests that Panama has performed well in terms of the first two of these goals and poorly in terms of the second two.

The rate of economic growth can hardly be considered a priority problem. Growth performance of the economy has been vigorous and sustained for more than a decade. There is little point, therefore, in simply striving to raise the growth rate by 1 or 2 percentage points per year. Attaining other goals becomes relatively more important.

The relative decline in the agricultural sector should be viewed in part as a response to changes in the composition of demand in the economy. As incomes rise, consumers demand more industrial products and services and spend a smaller proportion of their incomes on food. The relatively more rapid growth of the nonagricultural sectors provides the desired mix of goods and services. The transfer of human and financial resources from agriculture to the more rapidly growing sectors has been an essential element in the structural transformation of the Panamanian economy. Similarly, price stability has not been a pressing problem. Rapid growth has proceeded almost continuously under noninfla-

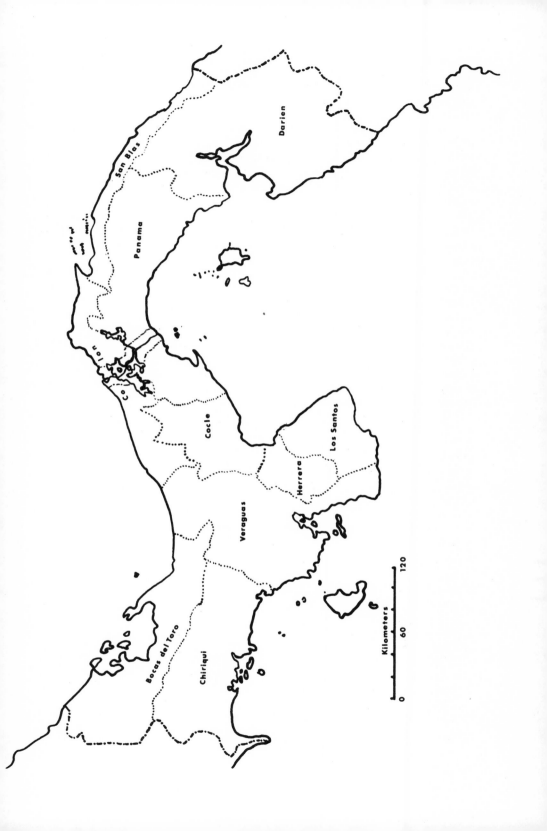

tionary conditions. Current price problems appear to signal poor output performance in agriculture rather than to indicate general price instability.

However, economic growth and price stability have been achieved under conditions of less than full and efficient utilization of resources. Unemployment has been a long-run problem in Panama City; it was estimated to be about 10% of the metropolitan work force in 1970. Underemployment is an even more serious problem; its presence is signaled by the large amount of labor in service and agricultural sectors where output per worker is much lower than in others. The amount of underemployed human resources that exists among campesino families because of the small size and low level of technology of their farms will be evaluated in Chapter 3.

Inefficient utilization of labor is related to the unequal distribution of income. The existing skewed distribution of income will become even more so if a considerable part of the population is bypassed by economic development. The concern with income inequality is especially relevant in the agricultural sector, considering the high incidence of rural poverty. Policies designed only to promote the most rapid growth in agricultural output are unlikely to trickle down to the economically marginal campesinos. The lot of the small, subsistence level farmers is likely to improve only if equity and efficiency goals are given priority along with output and stability objectives.

CHAPTER TWO

STRUCTURE
OF THE ECONOMY

MACROECONOMIC MODELS that quantify causal relationships among important variables can be extremely useful for planning and policy purposes. Economic planning requires an understanding of the structure of the economy and the nature of the growth process. Policy analysis is concerned with the consequences of alternative policy choices on structure, growth, and utilization of resources in the economy.

Since most macroeconomic models are highly aggregative, they do not take into account the interrelationships and intermediate product flows that exist among sectors of the economy. A Leontief input-output model can be used to examine these intersectoral relationships and to test the consistency of an overall rate of growth with sectoral growth paths. A macroeconomic model linked to an input-output table for the Panamanian economy is described in this chapter. The complete model is used to examine sectoral growth rates consistent with forecasted overall growth rates and with the implied intersectoral flows of intermediate goods among the various sectors of the economy.

AGGREGATE MACROECONOMIC MODEL

Variables in a model can be grouped into three categories: (1) endogenous variables whose values are determined within the system, (2) exogenous variables determined outside the system, and (3) predetermined variables determined within the system in a previous time period. Variables for the Panama model are listed below:

Endogenous Variables
C_t^P = private consumption expenditures in year t
Y_t^d = personal disposable income in year t

I_t^P = private investment expenditure in year t
C_t^G = government consumption expenditure in year t
Y_t = gross domestic product in year t
ΔS_t = changes in inventories in year t
M_t = imports of goods and services in year t
C_t = total consumption expenditures (both public and private) in year t
I_t = total investment expenditures (both public and private) in year t
T_t^D = direct taxes in year t
T_t^I = indirect taxes in year t

Exogenous Variables
X_t = total exports of goods and services in year t
I_t^G = government investment expenditures in year t

Predetermined Variables
C_{t-1}^P = private consumption expenditures in year t — 1
Y_{t-1} = gross domestic product in year t — 1

Equations for the aggregate model are shown below with estimates of the parameters, standard errors of the parameters (in parentheses), and t statistics.[1] The correlation coefficient (R^2), which measures the "goodness of fit," and the Durbin-Watson statistic (d),[2] which estimates the extent of serial correlation between the error terms in the equations, also are given for each equation. Parameters of the equations were estimated using ordinary least squares, except for those for which serial correlation was found to exist; parameters of the latter group were estimated by generalized least squares. Data for 1950–70 were used for the estimates.

(1a) $C_t^P = \underset{\substack{(0.1396)\\3.33**}}{0.4652\ Y_t^d} + \underset{\substack{(0.1798)\\2.59*}}{0.4656\ C_{t-1}^P}$ $R^2 = 0.9990$

(1b) $I_t^P = \underset{\substack{(5.48)\\-7.20**}}{-39.40} + \underset{\substack{(0.0111)\\20.88**}}{0.2390\ Y_{t-1}}$ $R^2 = 0.9603$ $d = 1.1482$

(1c) $C_t^G = \underset{\substack{(0.0042)\\26.95**}}{0.113\ Y_t}$ $R^2 = 0.9745$ $d = 2.21$

(1d) $\Delta S_t = \underset{\substack{(0.0246)\\12.91**}}{0.3173\ (Y_t - Y_{t-1})}$ $R^2 = 0.8976$ $d = 2.42$

1. * Indicates significance at 0.05 level. ** Indicates significance at 0.01 level.
2. d = 2.0 indicates that the null hypothesis of either positive or negative serial correlation is rejected. The Durbin-Watson statistic is not given for equation (1a), for which it is not a valid measure of serial correlation.

(1e) $\quad M_t = \quad 0.3437\ C_t\ +\ 0.6487\ I_t \qquad\qquad R^2 = 0.9946$
$\qquad\qquad\qquad (0.0273) \qquad (0.1072) \qquad\qquad\ \ d\ \ = 1.93$
$\qquad\qquad\qquad 12.6^{**} \qquad\quad\ \ 6.1^*$

(1f) $\quad T_t^D = \quad -26.33\ +\ 0.1151\ Y_t \qquad\qquad R^2 = 0.9750$
$\qquad\qquad\qquad (4.25) \quad (0.0074) \qquad\qquad\quad\ \ d\ \ = 1.80$
$\qquad\qquad\quad -6.20^{**} \quad 15.37^{**}$

(1g) $\quad T_t^I = \quad 0.0765\ Y_t \qquad\qquad\qquad\qquad R^2 = 0.9955$
$\qquad\qquad\qquad (0.0011) \qquad\qquad\qquad\qquad\ \ d\ \ = 1.35$
$\qquad\qquad\qquad 64.63^{**}$

(1h) $\quad C_t = C_t^P + C_t^G$

(1i) $\qquad Y_t = C_t^P + I_t^P + \Delta S_t + C_t^G + \overline{I}_t^G + \overline{X}_t - M_t$

(1j) $\qquad Y_t^d = Y_t - T_t^D - T_t^I$

(1k) $\qquad I_t = I_t^P + I_t^G$

Equation (1a) expresses private consumption expenditures as a function of personal disposable income and private consumption expenditures in the previous year. This formulation implies that past consumption, as well as present disposable income, affects present consumption, a formulation of the consumption function implied by the Friedman "permanent income" hypothesis. This form of the consumption function allows both the short-run and long-run marginal propensity to consume to be estimated. For this purpose, let

$$C_t^{P*} = a + bY_t$$

be the long-run equilibrium consumption function. The parameter (b) is the long-run marginal propensity to consume. Implicit in this definition is the assumption that consumers, given an increase in income, will require several years to fully readjust their consumption behavior. Assume the following partial adjustment mechanism:

$$(C_t^P - C_{t-1}^P) = \lambda(C_t^{P*} - C_{t-1}^P)$$

when C_t^P is actual observed consumption in time period t. Substituting the equation for C_t^{P*} into the above equation gives

$$(C_t^P - C_{t-1}^P) = \lambda(a + bY_t - C_{t-1}^P)$$

or

$$C_t^P = \lambda a + \lambda bY_t + (1-\lambda)\ C_{t-1}^P$$

which is the same equation as (1a) when $a = 0$. Estimates of the parameters in this equation give the short-run marginal propensity to consume (λb) and the long-run marginal propensity to consume (b). The estimated coefficients were:

$$\lambda = 0.5344, \qquad \lambda b = 0.4652, \qquad (1 - \lambda) = 0.4656$$

The short-run marginal propensity to consume (mpc) is 0.4652, and the long-run mpc is 0.8705, which implies a long-run savings propensity of 0.13. If personal disposable income were to increase by B/1 million, personal consumption expenditures would increase by B/465,200 in the same year. Eventually, consumers would adjust their consumption behavior to their higher income level, so that in the long run consumption would increase by B/870,500.

Equation (1b) expresses gross private capital formation as a function of lagged gross domestic product (GDP). The specification of an equation for investment is always a problem because capital formation is influenced by many quantitative and qualitative factors such as the relative price of capital, expectations regarding borrowing rates of interest, expectations regarding future sales, political instability, and expected performance of export earnings. Three alternative specifications for the private investment equation were estimated. First, an accelerator model was tried where private capital formation was expressed as a function of the change in income ($Y_t - Y_{t-1}$). This specification seems reasonable because expectations about the future are likely to be influenced more by changes in income than by actual levels of income. The estimated equation showed a highly significant relationship between private capital formation and $Y_t - Y_{t-1}$. However, problems arise with an accelerator function because private investment becomes highly dependent on errors in the model. For example, if income in period $t - 1$ is overestimated and income at t is underestimated, investment will be greatly underestimated. Since errors are compounded over time, the predictions from accelerator specification proved unsatisfactory in this model.

An alternative specification for private investment would relate private investment to lagged exports. This specification can be justified on the grounds that Panama's economy is export led. Growth of exports essentially determines investment and, therefore, growth of the economy. This function explained private investment reasonably well but was not included in the model because another function, equation (1b), gave slightly better predictions. Moreover, since exports constitute about 35% of total GDP, equation (1b) incorporates the causal effects of lagged exports, along with the effects of a high GDP in the previous year on the domestic production sector.

Equation (1c) expresses government consumption expenditures as a constant proportion of GDP. This specification assumes that as GDP increases, the demand for government services will increase, leading to larger government consumption expenditures.

Equation (1d) is designed to explain changes in inventories, but it is the least successful equation in the model as far as explaining the variation in the dependent variable. Serious problems, both of data and of economic theory, plague inventory equations. The specification that the change in inventories is a function of the change in GDP is reasonable if producers and merchants expect sales to increase following a rise in national income.

Equation (1e) relates imports to consumption and investment. This equation allows investment and consumption to have different import propensities. The estimated equation indicates that this difference exists in Panama. According to the estimates, a B/1 increase in investment will increase imports by B/0.65, while a B/1 increase in consumption will increase imports by only B/0.34. The higher import propensity for investment reflects the need to import both machinery and raw materials.

Equation (1f) relates direct taxes to GDP. According to the parameter estimates, the marginal direct tax rate is 0.12. The negative intercept indicates that the average direct tax rate increases as income increases, which suggests that direct taxes are progressive in their incidence.

Equation (1g) relates indirect taxes to GDP. The implied average and marginal indirect tax rate is about 0.08. The intercept term for this function was not significantly different from zero, an indication that indirect taxes are proportional to income.

Equations (1h)–(1k) are accounting identities required to close the model. The complete model contains 11 equations and 11 endogenous variables. Therefore, the values of the endogenous variables can be determined uniquely within the system, given the values of the exogenous and predetermined variables.

The model can be written compactly in matrix notation as

$$Ay = BX$$

where

A = an 11×11 matrix consisting of the coefficients of the endogenous variables

y = an 11×1 vector of the endogenous variables

B = an 11×6 matrix of the coefficients of the exogenous and predetermined variables (including the intercepts of the investment and direct tax functions)

X = a 6×1 vector of exogenous and predetermined variables (including the constant components of investment and direct taxes)

TABLE 2.1. • IMPACT-MULTIPLIER MATRIX DERIVED FROM THE MACROECONOMIC MODEL (EXOGENOUS AND PREDETERMINED VARIABLES)

Endogenous Variables	X_t	I_t^G	C_{t-1}^P	Y_{t-1}	T_o^D Autonomous Direct Taxes[a]	I_o^P Autonomous Investment[a]
Y_t	2.7660	0.9717	0.8452	-0.6454	-0.8445	0.9717
Y_t^d	2.2361	0.7855	0.6833	-0.5218	-1.6827	0.7855
C_t^P	1.0402	0.3654	0.7835	-0.2427	-0.7828	0.3654
C_t^G	0.3134	0.1101	0.0958	-0.0731	-0.0957	0.1101
I_t^P	0.0	0.0	0.0	0.2390	0.0	1.0000
ΔS_t	0.8777	0.3083	0.2682	-0.5221	-0.2680	0.3083
M_t	0.4652	0.8121	0.3022	0.0465	-0.3019	0.8121
T_t^D	0.3184	0.1118	0.0973	-0.0743	0.9028	0.1118
T_t^I	0.2116	0.0743	0.0647	-0.0494	-0.0646	0.0743
C_t	1.3536	0.4755	0.8792	-0.3158	-0.8785	0.4755
I_t	0.0	1.0000	0.0	0.2390	0.0	1.0000

Note: The impact of a one-unit change in an exogenous or predetermined variable on any endogenous variable can be found by locating the number corresponding to the row and column of selected endogenous and "given" variables (e.g., the effect of a B/1 increase in exports will increase imports B/0.47).

[a] Autonomous direct taxes and autonomous private investment should not be confused with endogenous direct taxes or private investment. T_o^D and I_o^P refer only to the intercept of the direct tax and private investment functions, respectively. The value of the multiplier for these terms measures the impact of an autonomous change or shift in the functions.

By taking the matrix inverse of A, the vector of endogenous variables can be expressed in terms of the exogenous and predetermined variables of the systems:

$$Y = A^{-1}BX$$

$A^{-1}B$ is an 11×6 matrix (the impact-multiplier matrix), which shows the changes that will result in any endogenous variable with a small change in any of the given variables. The impact-multiplier matrix derived from the empirical estimates of the parameters in the model is contained in Table 2.1.

Verification of the Model

Before using the model to forecast future growth, it was tested with the actual 1960–70 data, using the Theil inequality coefficient.[3] This coefficient is defined as

$$Z = \frac{\sqrt{\frac{1}{n} \sum_{i=1}^{n} (P_i - A_i)^2}}{\sqrt{\frac{1}{n} \sum_{i=1}^{n} P_i^2} + \sqrt{\frac{1}{n} \sum_{i=1}^{n} A_i^2}}$$

where

P_i = predicted value of the variable for observation i
A_i = actual value of the variable for observation i

The coefficient Z ranges from 0 to 1. If $Z = 0$, then $P = A$ for all observations and the forecasts are perfect. On the other hand, if $Z = 1$, the equation used to estimate the P_i has no predictive ability.

The Theil inequality coefficient was calculated for the model over the 1960–70 period for two different types of forecasts. The first test used the actual values of the predetermined variables C_{t-1}^P and Y_{t-1} and the exogenous variables in each year to generate the values of the endogenous variables. The second test was more stringent in that the values of C_t^P and Y_t for 1959 were used as the predetermined variables in predicting 1960 values of the endogenous variables, but for subsequent years the model generated its own lagged variables. The predicted values of GDP for the two tests are compared to actual GDP in Table 2.2.

3. Henri Theil, *Economic Forecasts and Policy*, Amsterdam: North-Holland Publishing Company, 1965, p. 32.

TABLE 2.2. • ACTUAL VERSUS PREDICTED VALUES OF GROSS DOMESTIC PRODUCT, 1960–
          70

Year	GDP (actual)	GDP, Test 1[a] (predetermined)	GDP, Test 2[b] (predetermined)
		(millions of 1960 balboas)	
1960	415.8	347.7	347.7
1961	460.9	413.3	423.0
1962	498.4	488.7	476.2
1963	541.5	536.3	524.3
1964	565.5	542.5	519.2
1965	617.3	623.2	606.6
1966	664.1	679.9	640.7
1967	720.9	728.8	719.1
1968	771.2	784.6	765.8
1969	836.3	826.1	831.3
1970	894.5	901.8	885.0

[a]Actual values of predetermined variables.

[b]Model-generated values of predetermined variables.

The values of Z for both tests indicate that the model predicts the endogenous variables very satisfactorily over the sample period (Table 2.3). The accuracy of future forecasts will be reduced, however, if structural changes in the economy change the values of the parameters.

Implications of the Model

Examination of the parameter estimates and the resulting impact-multiplier matrix leads to an important conclusion about the Panamanian economy; that is, exports have been the most important factor in the growth.

The impact-multiplier matrix shows the multiplier for exports equal to 2.766. This multiplier is the partial derivative of GDP with respect to

TABLE 2.3. ● THEIL INEQUALITY COEFFICIENT FOR THE MACROECONOMIC VARIABLES IN THE MODEL

Endogenous Variable	Test 1[a]	Test 2[b]
GDP	0.0211	0.0232
C^P	0.0241	0.0395
C^G	0.0231	0.0258
I^P	0.0582	0.0488
ΔS	0.2730	0.3102
M	0.0148	0.0248
T^D	0.0379	0.0360
T^I	0.0394	0.0374

[a] Actual values of predetermined variables.

[b] Model-generated values of predetermined variables.

exports $(\partial Y/\partial X)$. The elasticity of GDP with respect to exports is defined by

$$E_x = \frac{\partial Y}{\partial X} \frac{X}{Y}$$

This elasticity measures the percentage change in GDP resulting from a 1% change in exports. The value of the elasticity at a given X/Y ratio is determined by the export multiplier and the ratio of exports to GDP. The average ratio of exports to GDP for 1960–70 was 0.3542. Multiplying this ratio by 2.766 gives 0.9797, the value of the elasticity, which shows that a 1% increase in exports results in a 0.9797% increase in GDP.

The nearly one-to-one relationship between the growth rate of exports and the growth rate of the economy indicates the importance of exports. Clearly, the single most important determinant of the overall rate of growth in the model is the growth rate of exports. A breakdown of total exports into five categories is shown in Table 2.4. In 1970, goods and services sold to the Canal Zone (including the wages and salaries paid to residents of Panama who work in the Canal Zone) made up

TABLE 2.4. ● EXPORTS OF GOODS AND SERVICES, 1950–70

Year	Total	Canal Zone	Bananas	Tourism	Colon Free Zone	Others
			(millions of 1960 balboas)			
1950	109.8	77.4	12.5	4.5	0	15.4
1951	102.8	68.1	12.8	4.9	0	17.0
1952	102.7	68.0	10.3	5.6	0	18.8
1953	109.2	71.7	12.9	4.7	1.1	18.8
1954	105.1	65.7	16.9	5.7	1.2	15.6
1955	113.7	69.4	19.9	6.0	1.7	16.7
1956	113.5	69.3	17.5	7.9	2.5	16.3
1957	116.0	63.8	19.8	8.7	2.9	20.8
1958	110.0	55.4	18.2	9.7	3.1	23.6
1959	116.1	54.8	19.5	11.9	4.6	25.3
1960	127.3	65.4	18.2	11.8	6.3	25.6
1961	146.3	72.8	20.8	15.1	8.8	28.8
1962	175.9	86.6	19.0	17.5	8.5	44.3
1963	195.5	95.1	21.0	13.4	8.0	58.0
1964	196.0	87.0	21.5	13.3	9.3	64.9
1965	223.4	97.4	30.0	18.1	11.6	66.3
1966	245.1	104.5	33.3	22.4	14.0	70.9
1967	269.4	118.8	35.4	21.8	16.2	77.2
1968	289.7	130.6	40.8	21.6	16.2	80.5
1969	309.5	137.3	44.0	23.7	21.7	82.8
1970	324.5	129.3	42.6	32.9	28.2	91.5

Source:　Dirección de Estadística y Censo.

about 40% of total exports; bananas accounted for about 13%. Tourism, which includes expenditures by tourists, businessmen, visitors on official government business, and passengers in transit accounted for 10%. Value added to goods imported then reexported from the Colon Free Zone made up about 9%. Other goods and services, which include exports such as petroleum products, sugar, shrimp, and financial services, accounted for 28% of total exports. This breakdown also illustrates the importance of the Canal Zone to the overall performance of the Panamanian economy. A 1% increase in the growth rate of exports to the Canal Zone will increase the overall growth rate of the economy by about 0.39%.

The multiplier for government investment expenditures is only 0.9717. In other words, a B/1 increase in government investment increases total GDP by slightly less than B/1, and there is no multiplier effect of government investment. Although this measurement does not take into account the increase in total production capacity which may result from government investment and may affect future output, it does indicate that government investment expenditures used to stimulate the economy will have only limited short-run impact. The explanation for this apparent paradox can be found in equation (1e). Estimates of the parameters of the import function indicate that an increase of B/1 in investment increases imports by B/0.65. This leakage, resulting from the high-import content of investment, counteracts any multiplier effect that would otherwise result from investment expenditures.

In summary, exports are the most important growth factor in the model. Growth projections from the model, therefore, can be expected to be highly sensitive to export levels. Alternative export projections are developed and used later in this chapter to forecast growth in the economy for the 1971–75 period.

INPUT-OUTPUT MODEL

For purposes of developing an intersectoral framework for the economy, total GDP was disaggregated into ten sectoral outputs:

1. Agriculture, including forestry, hunting, fishing.
2. Mining and quarrying.
3. Food manufacturing, including beverages and tobacco.
4. Nonfood manufacturing.
5. Construction.
6. Utilities.
7. Commerce, including storage, communications, and transportation.
8. Finance.
9. Housing.
10. Services (public and private, including public administration).

With this aggregation, GDP is composed of ten "types" of goods. The total supply of goods of any type is equal to domestic production plus imports as in equation (2a):

$$(2a) \quad S_i = Q_i + M_i \qquad i = 1, \ldots, 10$$

where

S_i = total supply of goods of type i
Q_i = total domestic output of sector i
M_i = imports of goods of type i

The total supply of goods of type i is equal to the sum of inter-mediate demands from all sectors (including sector i) and the final demand for type i goods. This sum is given by equation (2b).

$$(2b) \quad S_i = \sum_{j=1}^{10} S_{ij} + F_i \qquad i = 1, \ldots, 10$$

$$j = 1, \ldots, 10$$

where

S_{ij} = supply of goods of type i to sector j
F_i = final demand for goods of type i

If domestic output of sector i is assumed to be a constant proportion of the total supply of goods produced in sector i, S_i and Q_i can be written $Q_i = U_i S_i$, which gives

$$(2c) \quad S_i = \frac{1}{U_i} Q_i \qquad i = 1, \ldots, 10$$

where U_i is the proportion of total supply of type i goods that is pro-duced domestically.

Define a_{ij} to be the amount of good i required to produce one unit of good j

$$a_{ij} = \frac{S_{ij}}{Q_j}$$

or

$$(2d) \quad S_{ij} = a_{ij} Q_j \qquad i = 1, \ldots, 10$$
$$j = 1, \ldots, 10$$

Substituting equations (2c) and (2d) into equation (2b) and bring-ing $\Sigma_{j=1}^{10} a_{ij} Q_j$ to the left-hand side gives

$$(2e) \quad \frac{Q_i}{U_i} - \sum_{j=1}^{10} a_{ij} \cdot Q_j = F_i \qquad \begin{array}{l} i = 1, \ldots, 10 \\ j = 1, \ldots, 10 \end{array}$$

The final demand component F_i is defined as

$$(2f) \quad F_i = C_i^P + I_i^P + C_i^G + I_i^G + X_i$$

where

C_i^P = private consumption demand for type i goods
I_i^P = private investment demand for type i goods
C_i^G = government consumption demand for type i goods
I_i^G = government investment demand for type i goods
X_i = exports of type i goods

Writing equation (2e) for all i and j gives the following system of equations:

$$
(2g)
\begin{aligned}
\frac{Q_1}{U_1} - a_{11}Q_1 - a_{12}Q_2 - a_{13}Q_3 - \ldots - a_{1,10}Q_{10} &= F_1 \\
\frac{Q_2}{U_2} - a_{21}Q_1 - a_{22}Q_2 - a_{23}Q_3 - \ldots - a_{2,10}Q_{10} &= F_2 \\
&\vdots \\
\frac{Q_{10}}{U_{10}} - a_{10,1}Q_1 - a_{10,2}Q_2 - a_{10,3}Q_3 - \ldots - a_{10,10}Q_{10} &= F_{10}
\end{aligned}
$$

The system of equations in (2g) can be written in matrix notation as

$$(2h) \quad (D - A)Q = F$$

where

$$
D = \begin{bmatrix}
\dfrac{1}{U_1} & & & \\
& \dfrac{1}{U_2} & & \\
& & \ddots & \\
& & & \dfrac{1}{U_{10}}
\end{bmatrix}
$$

$$A = \begin{bmatrix} -a_{11} & - & a_{12} & \cdots & - & a_{1,10} \\ -a_{21} & - & a_{22} & \cdots & - & a_{2,10} \\ & \cdot & & & & \\ & \cdot & & & & \\ & \cdot & & & & \\ -a_{10,1} & - & a_{10,2} & \cdots & - & a_{10,10} \end{bmatrix}$$

$$Q = \begin{bmatrix} Q_1 & & & \\ & Q_2 & & \\ & & \cdot & \\ & & & \cdot \\ & & & & Q_{10} \end{bmatrix}$$

$$F = \begin{bmatrix} C_1^P + I_1^P + C_1^G + I_1^G + X_1 \\ C_2^P + I_2^P + C_2^G + I_2^G + X_2 \\ \cdot \\ \cdot \\ \cdot \\ C_{10}^P + I_{10}^P + C_{10}^G + I_{10}^G + X_{10} \end{bmatrix}$$

If the 10×10 matrix $(D - A)$ is nonsingular, the system can be solved uniquely for gross sectoral outputs consistent with any given level of final demand. Finding the matrix inverse of $D - A$ and multiplying by equation (2h) gives the following solution:

(2i) $\quad Q = (D - A)^{-1}F$

Equation (2i) can be used to calculate gross output of each sector if final demand for goods from each sector (including imports) is known or can be projected. The actual D, A, and $(D - A)^{-1}$ matrices for Panama are given in Tables B.1, B.2, and B.3 of the Appendix. The coefficients for the A matrix were derived from a 50-sector input-output table based on 1961 data.

If sectoral value added is assumed to be a constant proportion of gross sectoral production, value added by sector at market prices can be defined as follows:

$$V_i = a_i Q_i$$

where

V_i = value added in sector i
Q_i = total domestic output of sector i
a_i = a constant proportion

Let a be the diagonal matrix with proportions of sectoral value added to total output as the diagonal elements:

$$a = \begin{bmatrix} a_1 & & & & \\ & a_2 & & & \\ & & \cdot & & \\ & & & \cdot & \\ & & & & a_{10} \end{bmatrix}$$

Then,

$$V = {}_aQ$$

or substituting for Q,

$$(2j) \quad V = {}_a(D - A)^{-1}F$$

where value added by sector is now expressed in terms of final demand.

Estimation of the a_i's was difficult because gross production data are published for the agricultural and manufacturing sectors only. Therefore, for these two sectors, the ratio of value added to gross production for 1970 was used.[4] Since no gross output data are available for the other sectors, the ratio of value added to gross output implied by the data given in the input-output table (based on 1961 data) was used to obtain the initial estimates of the a's. The a vector was then adjusted so that the model predicted value added reasonably well for 1970, which served as a benchmark year (Table 2.5). The model adjusted in this manner was used to predict value added by sector for the 1971–75 period.

The values of a's given in Table 2.5 reflect the extent to which the various sectors are dependent upon intermediate goods for production. Tertiary industries such as services, housing, and finance, for example, require very little intermediate inputs, nor do the extractive industries of agriculture and mining. As a result, value added is high relative to the total value of output in these sectors. However, manufacturing (especially food) has strong backward linkage effects; i.e., requirements

4. Gross production data for these sectors in 1970 can be found in Informe Económico, 1971, Dirección General de Planificación y Administración, November 1972.

TABLE 2.5. ● SECTOR VALUE ADDED AS A PROPORTION OF GROSS SECTORAL OUTPUT

Sector	$\alpha_{i,}$
Agriculture	0.8587
Mining	0.8862
Food Manufacturing	0.4517
Nonfood Manufacturing	0.5539
Construction	0.5000
Utilities	0.6614
Commerce	0.8142
Finances	0.9202
Housing	0.9897
Services	0.8783

for intermediate inputs are high. For example, in food manufacturing, value added is equal to only 45% of gross output.

The a's may change over time. In general, industry dependence on intermediate inputs grows as development proceeds. The agricultural sector is a good example. In early stages of development, agricultural output is largely a function of the land and labor resources in the sector. Adoption of new technology increases the use of fertilizer, chemicals, machinery, and other purchased inputs, which reduces the ratio of value added to gross output in the sector.

Sectors in which the ratio of value added to gross output is high can grow without simultaneous growth in the other sectors and, therefore, will not be affected to any great extent by bottlenecks, work stoppages, or miscellaneous problems that limit production in other sectors. However, a high ratio of value added to gross output also implies that growth in a particular sector will not create a strong demand for the goods produced by others or stimulate growth in those sectors. As a result, sectors such as housing and finance, while contributing directly to growth on the final demand side, are not "leading sectors" and do not have strong backward linkages with others through intersectoral flows of intermediate goods.

If average labor productivity in each sector remains constant, employment by sector can be derived from the following equation:

$$(2k) \quad E_i = e_i \cdot v_i$$

where $1/e_i$ is the average productivity of labor in sector i. Using this relationship, aggregate growth can be related to sectoral employment. An overall growth rate can then be analyzed in terms of sectoral growth in employment as well as sectoral growth in output.

GROWTH AND SECTORAL OUTPUT IN A CONSISTENCY FRAMEWORK

In this section, the aggregative macroeconomic model and the input-output model are combined in a total consistency framework in order to obtain consistent projections. It is possible that a growth rate of total GDP, if projected using an aggregative model, will not be consistent with the intersectoral relationships that exist in the economy. The input-output model takes these relationships into account and can be used to determine the sectoral growth rates consistent with an overall rate in the economy.

Figure 2.1 is a schematic representation of the total consistency framework. The framework is constructed by using the macroeconomic model to generate estimates of total aggregate demand. Exports and government investment are the exogenous variables to be projected outside the model. Total aggregate demand is then allocated among sectors, using weights based on sectoral consumption, investment, and export data to form the final demand vector F. Given F, it is possible to solve for gross output by sector using equation (2i) of the input-output model. Next, value added by sector is calculated using equation (2j). These projections of value added by sector are tested for consistency by determining if their sum is sufficiently close to the overall GDP generated by the model. The check cannot be exact due to statistical errors. Nevertheless, if the sum of value added by sector is reasonably close, the entire model is consistent. If the sum is different from projected GDP, the original GDP must be readjusted, which in turn changes the demand components and the estimates of sectoral value added. The process is iterated until a set of consistent estimates is found. Given the sectoral output projection, sectoral employment can be predicted by using equation (2k) of the input-output model.

PROJECTIONS OF COMPONENTS OF GDP AND SECTOR VALUE ADDED

The predictive power of any model depends upon the constancy of the model's parameters. Any major structural changes in the economy may invalidate the model's projections. For this reason, the model estimated in this study was used to make projections for the relatively

FIGURE 2.1 • PANAMA: CONSISTENCY BETWEEN OVERALL AND SECTOR GROWTH RATES

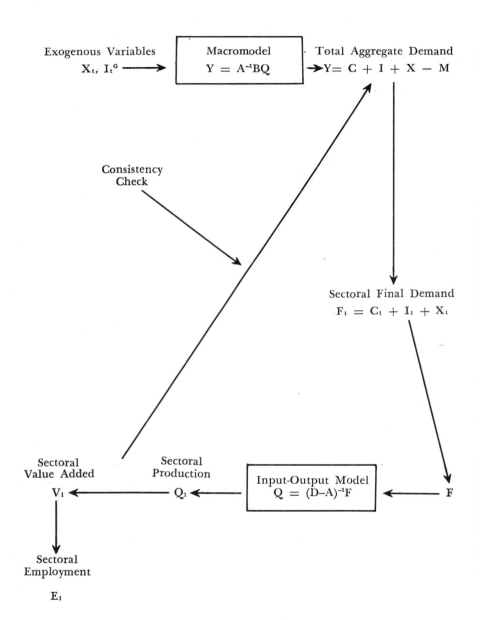

short time period 1971 through 1975. The preliminary data for 1971 were used to check the predicted values of GDP and sectoral value added for 1971.

Since the accuracy of the forecasts of the endogenous variables depends upon the accuracy of the projections of the exogenous variables and since the system in Panama is highly responsive to changes in exports, three sets of projections of the exogenous variables were developed in order to establish a range of values for the endogenous variables. The alternative projections are presented below.

Alternative A

Projections for exports (X_t) and government expenditures (I_t^G) were obtained using the following equations:

$$X_t = (1 + r_x)^t X_{1970}$$

$$I_t^G = (1 + r_g)^t I_{1970}^G$$

where X_{1970} and I_{1970}^G are the values of exports and government investment for 1970, respectively. The growth rates (r_x and r_g) were estimated by fitting the following equations by ordinary least squares for the 1950–70 period to obtain

$$X_t - X_{t-1} = r_x X_{t-1} = 0.07 X_{t-1}$$

$$I_t^G - I_{t-1}^G = r_g I_{t-1}^G = 0.16 I_{t-1}^G$$

The projections of the endogenous variables obtained by using these alternative A growth rates are based on the assumption that the exogenous variables will continue to grow at their average historical rate.

Alternative B

Projections of government investment, based on the Panamanian government's 1971–75 development plan, with some rephasing in expenditure outlays and disbursement on projects to be executed with foreign assistance, were developed by the World Bank in 1971.[5] Alternative B used the actual level of government investment in 1970 and the annual growth rates implied by World Bank investment projections.

---

5. International Bank for Reconstruction and Development, Memorandum on Recent Economic Developments and Prospects of Panama, Report CA-NA, July 9, 1971.

These are:

Year	$r_g(\%)$
1971	9.9
1972	5.7
1973	27.2
1974	4.2
1975	—6.7

Alternative B projections of government investment were somewhat lower than alternative A projections.

Alternative B assumed that total exports would grow at the same rate implied by World Bank projections of merchandise exports. This assumption resulted in the following annual growth rates:

Year	$r_x(\%)$
1971	14.0
1972	11.8
1973	8.4
1974	7.8
1975	9.5

Alternative B projections of exports are higher than alternative A projections.

Alternative C

Alternative C is a combination of alternatives A and B. The lower projections of exports used in alternative A and the lower projections of government investment used in alternative B were combined to form alternative C.

Projections for 1971–75

Projections for exports and government investment under the three alternatives are presented in Table 2.6. Projections of the endogenous variables of the model are given in Table 2.7 for the three alternative projections of the exogenous variables. Projections of value added for the ten sectors of the input-output model are presented in Table 2.8. Preliminary estimates from the national accounts data for 1971 are given in parentheses under the corresponding projected value. The total of value added for all sectors also is calculated and presented in Table 2.8. Comparison of this sum with the projected level of GDP for each year provides the consistency check explained earlier.

The contribution to GDP by the Canal Zone is not calculated by the input-output model. Therefore, to compare the sum of value added by sector (for the ten sectors) with total GDP, one must account for the

TABLE 2.6. • PROJECTED EXPORTS AND GOVERNMENT INVESTMENT, 1971–75

Year	Alternative A	Alternative B	Alternative C
	(millions of 1960 balboas)		
	Exports		
1971	347.2	369.9	347.2
1972	371.5	414.3	371.5
1973	397.5	447.5	397.5
1974	425.3	483.3	425.3
1975	455.1	531.6	455.1
	Government Investment		
1971	68.4	64.8	64.8
1972	79.4	68.5	68.5
1973	92.1	87.2	87.2
1974	106.8	90.8	90.8
1975	123.9	84.7	84.7

Canal Zone's contribution. For example, in 1971 the sum of value added for the ten sectors was B/915.1 million for alternative A. If the estimated contribution to GDP by the Canal Zone given in the national accounts is added to this figure, a GDP of B/987.0 million results. The projected total GDP given by the model is B/959.0 million, about 2.9% below the actual 1971 value. Since the input-output table was based on 1961 data, this difference seems to be sufficiently small to be considered consistent. With an up-to-date input-output table, it would be reasonable to expect greater accuracy. A check of the results for the other alternatives yields similar results. The projected growth rates for GDP of 8.4%, 10.3%, and 7.7% under alternatives A, B, and C, respectively, were accepted as consistent with the projected sectoral growth rates.

Value added for agriculture, however, was consistently overestimated, while the projections of value added for the rest of the sectors were reasonably accurate. This result might be attributed to weather

TABLE 2.7. • PROJECTIONS OF GROSS DOMESTIC PRODUCT AND COMPONENTS, 1971–75

Year	GDP	Y^d	C^P	C^G	I^P	ΔS	M	T^D	T^I	C^T	I^T
					(millions of 1960 balboas)						
					Alternative A						
1971	959.0 (977.6)	801.6	662.4 (667.6)	108.7 (114.9)	174.4	20.5	422.5	84.1	73.4	771.1	242.8
1972	1029.6	858.7	707.9	116.7	189.8	22.4	458.0	92.2	78.8	824.5	269.2
1973	1106.7	921.0	758.0	125.4	206.7	24.5	497.4	101.1	84.7	883.4	298.8
1974	1190.5	988.8	812.9	134.9	225.1	26.6	541.1	110.7	91.1	947.8	331.9
1975	1281.9	1062.6	872.8	145.2	245.1	29.0	589.3	121.2	98.1	1018.0	369.0
					Alternative B						
1971	1018.3 (977.6)	849.5	684.7 (667.6)	115.4 (114.9)	174.4	39.3	430.1	90.9	77.9	800.1	239.2
1972	1118.0	930.1	751.5	126.7	204.0	31.6	478.6	102.3	85.5	878.2	272.5
1973	1220.1	1012.6	821.0	138.2	227.8	32.4	534.0	114.1	93.3	959.2	315.0
1974	1315.4	1089.7	889.2	149.0	252.2	30.3	579.3	125.1	100.6	1078.2	343.0
1975	1439.2	1189.8	967.5	163.1	275.0	39.3	621.9	139.3	110.1	1130.6	359.7
					Alternative C						
1971	955.5 (977.6)	798.8	661.1 (667.6)	108.3 (114.9)	174.4	19.4	419.6	83.6	73.1	764.4	239.2
1972	1020.2	851.0	703.7	115.6	189.0	20.5	448.6	91.1	78.0	819.3	257.5
1973	1104.5	919.2	755.3	125.1	204.4	26.8	491.8	100.8	84.5	880.4	291.6
1974	1174.0	975.4	805.4	133.0	224.6	22.1	527.1	108.8	89.8	938.4	315.4
1975	1248.1	1035.3	856.6	141.4	241.2	23.5	554.4	117.3	95.5	998.0	325.9

Source: Model in this chapter.

conditions unfavorable to agriculture in 1970 and to the possibility that this sector had not totally recovered by 1971.

Although the model predicted well over the sample period, there was a tendency to underestimate GDP by a constant factor; but the growth rate of the predicted and actual values of GDP appear to be virtually identical. Therefore, more confidence can be placed in the

TABLE 2.8. • PROJECTED VALUE ADDED BY SECTOR

(millions of 1960 balboas)

Year	Agriculture	Mining and Quarrying	Food Manuf.	Nonfood Manuf.	Constr. Util.	Trans., etc.	Finance	Housing	Services	All Factors
Alternative A										
1971	187.4	2.8	68.2	91.4	62.5	31.0	199.0	38.3	66.8	167.7	915.1
	(167.9)	(2.6)	(69.3)	(97.2)	(63.6)	(29.7)	(203.9)	(39.4)	(66.0)	(159.9)	
1972	200.4	3.1	73.0	99.0	69.7	33.2	213.8	41.0	71.4	173.0	977.6
1973	214.8	3.4	78.2	107.4	77.8	35.6	230.0	44.0	76.6	185.3	1053.1
1974	230.3	3.8	83.9	116.7	86.9	38.2	247.5	47.2	82.2	198.7	1135.4
1975	247.3	4.2	90.1	126.9	97.2	41.1	266.7	50.8	88.3	213.1	1225.7
Alternative B										
1971	197.2	2.9	71.2	94.1	61.8	32.8	218.5	40.2	69.8	169.8	958.3
	(167.9)	(2.6)	(69.3)	(97.2)	(63.6)	(29.7)	(203.9)	(39.4)	(66.0)	(159.9)	
1972	216.4	3.2	78.4	104.7	69.5	36.2	234.5	44.0	76.5	187.9	1051.3
1973	235.6	3.6	85.4	116.4	81.1	39.4	255.2	48.0	83.5	204.3	1152.5
1974	254.6	4.0	92.4	126.2	87.7	42.5	273.2	51.8	90.2	220.8	1243.4
1975	278.4	4.2	100.8	176.1	91.0	46.5	301.3	56.6	93.4	241.5	1354.8
Alternative C										
1971	186.9	2.8	68.1	90.8	61.3	30.9	197.9	38.1	66.6	161.4	904.8
	(167.9)	(2.6)	(69.3)	(97.2)	(63.6)	(29.7)	(203.9)	(39.4)	(66.0)	(159.9)	
1972	199.3	3.0	72.6	97.2	65.8	33.0	211.0	40.6	70.9	172.2	965.7
1973	214.4	3.4	78.0	106.4	75.7	33.5	230.5	43.9	76.4	184.9	1049.1
1974	228.2	3.6	83.1	114.0	81.3	37.9	242.2	46.6	81.3	197.3	1115.5
1975	243.0	3.8	88.5	120.3	83.0	40.3	257.3	49.5	86.5	210.4	1182.5

Source: Input-output model in this chapter.

projected growth rates of the variables than in the absolute values. Table 2.9 presents the average projected growth rate over the 1971–75 period for GDP and sectoral value added under the three alternative projections.

It is important to understand the assumptions underlying these projections. An input-output model assumes that there are no other constraints on sectoral output other than those accounted for by the intersectoral flows of intermediate goods. Basically, the assumption is

TABLE 2.9. • **CONSISTENT ANNUAL GROWTH RATES OF OVERALL AND SECTORAL GROSS DOMESTIC PRODUCT**

Sector	Alternative A	Alternative B	Alternative C
	(1971-75 average)		
GDP	8.4	10.3	7.7
Agriculture	8.0	10.3	7.5
Mining and Quarrying	12.5	11.2	8.9
Manufacturing[a]	9.0	10.8	7.9
Construction	13.9	11.8	8.8
Utilities	8.1	12.4	7.6
Transportation, etc.	8.5	9.5	7.5
Finance	8.2	10.2	7.7
Housing	8.0	10.2	7.5
Services	8.0	10.6	7.6

[a]Sum of food manufacturing and nonfood manufacturing.

that quantities supplied and demanded will be equal in each sector; i.e., that prices will adjust to equate supply and demand. These sectoral growth rates are, therefore, the required rates of growth that will equate supply and demand at 'constant prices. The growth rate of sector i in nominal terms is equal to the growth rate of real output plus the rate of price inflation for the sector. If the rate of real growth in a sector is sufficient to meet increasing demand, these projected rates of growth are equivalent to the real rates of growth. However, if there are other constraints on output (e.g., weather and land availability in agriculture), the projected rates of growth will be equal to the nominal rates and thus greater than the real rate since prices must rise to equate supply and demand. The relationship between real and nominal growth rates explains the similarity in projected rates for all sectors (Table 2.9), while the real rates of growth of the sectors have been quite different in the past. As shown in Chapter 1, there have been substantial differences among sectors with respect to price increases. Consequently, even if nominal sectoral growth rates were equal, real sectoral rates would be quite different.

Table 2.9 shows that an 8% real rate of growth in the agricultural sector is consistent with an 8% overall growth in GDP. This rate for agriculture is almost double the historical rate, especially since 1965, while the projected overall growth rate is about equal to that of the 1960–70 period. If this higher rate of growth in agricultural output cannot be achieved, overall growth in the economy is likely to be constrained in the following ways: (1) pressures on food prices will continue and intensify, leading to overall price instability; (2) exports will be insufficient, and the rate of growth will fall; and (3) other industries will be unable to obtain as large quantities of intermediate goods from the agricultural sector as they need, thus creating bottlenecks elsewhere in the economy. It is in this sense that agriculture in Panama can be termed a lagging sector.

EMPLOYMENT PROJECTIONS

Given the projections of sectoral growth rates, estimates of the growth rates of employment by sector (N_i) can be obtained using the following equation:

$$\%\Delta N_i = E_{ei}\%\Delta Q_i$$

where E_{ei} is the elasticity of sectoral employment with respect to sectoral real output. The sector employment elasticities were estimated, using the arc elasticity formula and data based on changes in employment and output between 1960 and 1970.

The elasticities of employment and projected annual growth rates of sectoral employment under the three alternative projections are shown in Table 2.10. The annual rates of growth of sectoral employment are projected under the following assumptions: (1) the projected rate of growth of output is equal to the real rate of growth for each sector (i.e., prices remain constant) and (2) the elasticity of employment for each sector remains constant and is equal to the 1960–70 elasticity.

An employment output elasticity of 1.16 for the utilities sector at first appears to be rather high because utilities are usually considered a capital-intensive sector. However, in a country where much of the infrastructure does not exist, a high-employment output elasticity for this sector reflects the more labor-intensive activities involved in infrastructure construction. Construction and services also show high-employment output elasticities.

For agriculture, the model predicts a low but positive growth rate of employment. In reality, agriculture is reaching the point where employment will soon reach a maximum and begin to decline. The maximum point cannot be predicted with the linear model used previously. To ascertain the time at which the turning point in the agricultural labor force might occur, an alternative approach was devised.

TABLE 2.10. • PROJECTED ANNUAL GROWTH RATES OF EMPLOYMENT BY SECTOR, 1971–75

Sector	E_{ei}	Alternative A	Alternative B	Alternative C
		(%)		
Agriculture	0.09	0.72	0.92	0.68
Manufacturing	0.77	6.9	8.3	6.1
Construction	1.01	14.0	11.9	8.9
Utilities	1.16	9.4	14.4	8.8
Commerce	0.73	6.2	6.9	5.5
Finance	0.72	5.9	7.3	5.5
Services	0.96	7.7	10.2	7.3

If the unemployment rate and the labor force participation rate for agriculture and nonagriculture are assumed constant, the growth rate of agricultural employment can be related to the growth rate of total employment and that in nonagriculture by the following equation:

$$r_A = \frac{L_T}{L_T - L_N} r_T - \frac{L_N}{L_T - L_N} r_N$$

where

r_A = rate of growth of agricultural employment
r_N = rate of growth of nonagricultural employment
r_T = rate of growth of total employment
L_T = total employment in the economy
L_N = employment in nonagriculture

The rate of growth of employment in agriculture will remain temporarily constant as long as the ratio of total employment to agricultural employment $[L_T/(L_T - L_N)]$ and the ratio of nonagricultural employment to agricultural employment $[L_N/(L_T - L_N)]$ remain constant over time. These ratios remain constant only if $r_T = r_N$. However, if $r_N > r_T$, the rate of growth in agricultural employment will become negative at some point in time. If $L_T = (1 + r_T)^t L_T^o$ and $L_N = (1 + r_N)^t L_N^o$, where L_T^o and L_N^o are equal to total employment and nonagricultural employment in the initial time period, respectively, and substituting into the expression for r_A, the rate of growth of agricultural employment can be expressed as a function of time (assuming r_T and r_N are constant over time). Thus

$$r_A(t) = Z(t)r_T - X(t)r_N$$

where

$$Z(t) = \frac{(1 + r_T)^t L_T{}^\circ}{(1 + r_T)^t L_T{}^\circ - (1 + r_N)^t L_N{}^\circ}$$

and

$$X(t) = \frac{(1 + r_N)^t L_N{}^\circ}{(1 + r_T)^t L_T{}^\circ - (1 + r_N)^t L_N{}^\circ}$$

Starting with 1970 as the base year, $r_A(t)$ was calculated for succeeding years. The growth rates for total and nonagricultural employment (r_T and r_N) were calculated on the basis of the growth rates implied by alternative A, which was based on the assumption that exports and government expenditure would grow at the same average rate as in the past. The derived values for r_T and r_N were 5.78% and 8.31%, respectively. The results of this test showed that agricultural employment would reach a peak by 1975. The calculations indicated that the labor force in agriculture would number about 162,000 workers at its peak, compared to 158,000 in 1970.

SUMMARY AND IMPLICATIONS

The model presented in this chapter supports the hypothesis that growth in exports is the most important determinant of the growth rate of the economy. Projections for 1971–75 indicate that exports must increase in the future as they have in the past if the economy is to continue to grow at a rate of 8% or more per year. Since a large part of merchandise exports originate in the agricultural sector, prospects for agricultural exports are important for maintaining a high rate of growth. Export possibilities for bananas, sugar, meat, and shrimp are discussed in Chapter 4.

The consistency check for the model verified that the growth rate of the agricultural sector must be increased to support continued overall growth in the economy at a rate of 8% or more. A coordinated development plan for the sector should identify output goals and supply possibilities specifically by product, region, and type of farm. Land utilization and production patterns are investigated in Chapter 3. Projections of domestic demand are contained in Chapter 4.

The point at which the agricultural labor force peaks and begins to decline should occur soon. If the economy continues to grow as rapidly and follows the same patterns in the 1970s as in the 1960s, peak employment in the agricultural sector will be reached by 1975. The effects of this evolution of the agricultural labor force for labor utilization and productivity in the sector will be considered in Chapter 3.

CHAPTER THREE

UTILIZATION OF AGRICULTURAL RESOURCES

AGRICULTURAL DEVELOPMENT concerns not only the production and utilization of agricultural products but also the welfare of farmers and their families. When income distribution, employment, and welfare objectives are considered along with output goals, analysis cannot be limited to the aggregate sector level. Factors such as farm size, tenancy arrangements, cropping patterns, and technology must be taken into account in identifying problems and evaluating alternative policies, programs, and projects. These factors define the economic structure of the sector and determine not only output but also productivity of the sector's resources and distribution of the income among farm families. If improvements in income distribution, employment, and welfare are to be achieved, target groups of farmers must be identified clearly and programs to reach those groups implemented effectively.

AREA IN FARMS

Only slightly more than one-fourth of the total land area in Panama was in farms in 1970 (Table 3.1), a proportion that has been increasing steadily since 1950. The total area in farms (2 million hectares in 1970) has nearly doubled since 1950. Herrera and Los Santos are the only provinces that had more than 50% of their total area incorporated in farms in 1970 (65.6% and 72.6%, respectively). Three other provinces (Cocle, Chiriqui, and Veraguas) had between one-third and one-half of their land in farms. The smallest proportions of total land in farms were in Darien (1.4%) and Bocas del Toro (5.2%).

In absolute terms, the provinces with the largest areas in farms in 1970 were Veraguas (433,495 hectares) and Chiriqui (42,268 hectares), followed by Panama, Los Santos, Cocle, and Herrera provinces listed in

TABLE 3.1. • AREA IN FARMS, BY PROVINCE, 1950, 1960, AND 1970

Province	Total Area (ha)	1950 Area in farms (ha)	1950 Percent of total	1960. Area in farms (ha)	1960. Percent of total	1970[a] Area in farms (ha)	1970[a] Percent of total
Bocas del Toro	891,700	30,311	3.4	58,132	6.5	46,164	5.2
Cocle	503,500	123,829	24.6	184,042	36.6	228,897	45.5
Colon	746,500	35,699	4.8	72,052	9.6	114,461	15.3
Chiriqui	875,800	343,945	39.3	434,727	49.6	421,268	48.1
Darien	1,680,300	17,056	1.0	35,784	2.1	23,324	1.4
Herrera	242,700	122,502	50.5	165,506	68.1	159,232	65.6
Los Santos	386,700	168,195	43.5	247,039	63.9	281,156	72.6
Panama	1,129,200	135,340	12.0	252,941	22.4	311,371	27.6
Veraguas	1,108,600	182,208	16.4	356,229	32.1	433,495	39.1
Total	7,565,000	1,159,082	15.3	1,806,452	23.9	2,019,368	26.7

Source: Segundo y Tercer Censo Agropecuario, 1960 and 1970. 1970 data are preliminary.

Note: The data for 1960 and 1970 included farms of 0.5 hectares and larger. The 1950 data were for farms 1.0 hectares and larger. As a result, the comparative increases for 1960 and 1970 are slightly over-stated.

[a] These are preliminary figures. Final figures for 1970 show a total of 2,098,068 hectares in farms and show figures for provinces somewhat different from those in the table. However, since no final data by farm size have been published, the preliminary figures were used in this report.

order of magnitude. Final census figures for 1970 show that land area in farms declined in Bocas del Toro and Darien provinces. Between 1960 and 1970, the largest increase in land in farms took place in Veraguas. Other provinces in which substantial extensions have taken place are Cocle, Los Santos, and Panama.

Some additional land has been incorporated in farms in Panama through spontaneous colonization. This process is occurring in Bocas del Toro, Darien, Colon, and Panama provinces. Immigrants to the new areas are largely small farmers and landless laborers from Chiriqui, Veraguas, Herrera, Los Santos, and Cocle provinces. These immigrants settle where new roads or rivers provide access to unsettled land. They mainly practice "slash and burn" agriculture methods that deplete the soil and provide low levels of living.

LAND UTILIZATION

About 10% of the total area in farms (199,010 hectares) was used for annual crop production in 1970 (Table 3.2). An additional 5% (100,294 hectares) was used for the production of perennial crops. Adding land in crop production to the 210,987 hectares that were fallow in 1970 gives a total cropland of about 500,000 hectares, which represented approximately one-fourth of the total land area in farms.

Three provinces (Cocle, Chiriqui, and Veraguas) accounted for more than half the land devoted to annual crop production in 1970. Chiriqui was also the leading province in perennial crops, contributing about 25% of the national total. The remaining perennial crop area was distributed over the country with five provinces contributing 9% to 15% each.

The biggest use of farmland in 1970 was for pastures. Almost half the total farm area (938,714 hectares) was in improved pastures; an additional 173,102 hectares were used as natural pasture. Together, improved and natural pastures accounted for 55% of the total farm area in 1970. Chiriqui had more land in improved pasture than any other province in 1970, followed in order by Los Santos, Veraguas, and Panama. Together, these four provinces accounted for more than three-fourths of the improved pastureland. The remaining 20% of the farm area consisted of forests, mountains, and other land classified as unproductive for crops and livestock.

Data on land utilization in 1960 is available for comparison to the 1970 pattern. In 1960, the total farm area was 1,803,502 hectares. Of this total, 30% was used for cropland, 45% was used for pastures, and the remaining 25% was unproductive. The most significant change in land use patterns by 1970 was that pastureland had been increased to 55% of the total, and cropland had fallen to 25%. In absolute terms,

TABLE 3.2. ● UTILIZATION OF LAND IN FARMS, 1970

Province	Area in Farms (ha)	Annual Crops		Perennial Crops		Fallow Land	
		Ha	%	Ha	%	Ha	%
Bocas del Toro	46,164	2,109	4.6	9,204	19.9	6,412	13.9
Cocle	228,897	37,316	16.3	14,396	6.3	31,122	13.6
Colon	114,461	11,248	9.8	11,271	9.9	15,356	13.4
Chiriqui	421,268	43,814	10.4	25,853	6.2	31,340	7.4
Darien	23,324	3,540	15.2	2,070	8.9	5,054	21.7
Herrera	159,232	19,109	12.0	5,643	3.5	13,008	8.2
Los Santos	281,156	18,672	6.6	4,005	1.4	11,538	4.1
Panama	311,371	20,365	6.6	13,441	4.3	30,614	9.8
Veraguas	433,495	42,837	9.9	14,411	3.3	66,543	15.4
Total	2,019,368	199,010	9.8	100,294	5.0	210,987	10.4

TABLE 3.2. ● (CONTINUED)

Province	Improved Pasture		Natural Pasture		Other Uses	
	Ha	%	Ha	%	Ha	%
Bocas del Toro	7,754	16.8	1,855	4.0	18,828	40.8
Cocle	76,893	33.6	23,104	10.1	46,066	20.1
Colon	41,606	36.4	5,420	4.7	29,560	25.8
Chiriqui	234,715	55.7	39,212	8.3	46,334	11.0
Darien	5,790	24.8	2,572	11.0	4,298	18.4
Herrera	80,533	50.6	18,424	11.6	22,515	14.1
Los Santos	188,880	67.2	18,113	6.5	39,948	14.2
Panama	142,626	45.8	29,977	9.6	74,348	23.9
Veraguas	159,917	36.9	34,425	7.9	115,362	26.6
Total	938,714	46.5	173,102	8.6	397,261	19.7

Source: Tercer Censo Agropecuario, Cifras Preliminares, p. 6.

pasture area rose from 819,000 to 1,112,000 hectares, while cropland fell from 551,000 to 510,000 hectares. The decrease in area actually used for crops (excluding fallow) was from 328,000 hectares in 1960 to 299,000 hectares in 1970.

In general, land in farms does not appear to be used very intensively, especially pastureland. Average yields for most crops are low relative to other countries. Data on yields are discussed in Chapter 4, which also contains a more extended analysis of livestock production systems. In 1970, 1.1 million hectares of pasture, 94% of which was classified as improved, was used for only 1.2 million head of cattle. Besides this low land-cattle ratio, animal productivity was also low. A more intensive system of livestock production would increase the carrying capacity of pastureland and raise productivity of the animals.

A preliminary survey of soil resources was published in 1971.[1] Soils in every province were assigned to classes II through VIII. In general, land with soils in classes II through IV are considered suitable for annual crops as well as for forests and pastures. Land with soil in classes V through VII are generally restricted to tree crops, pastures, and forests except for class V soil where drainage makes rice production possible. Land with soil of class VIII is generally not suitable for economic use. Almost 25% of Panama's total area was classified II through IV. More than 50% was placed in classes VI and VII. These data suggest that only a third to a fourth of suitable land is used for farms.

NUMBER AND SIZE OF FARMS

The number and size distributions of farms for 1960 and 1970 are shown in Table 3.3. The number of farms decreased from 107,946 to 103,631 in the ten-year period. For farms of 0.5 hectares or more, the decrease was from 95,505 to 90,942. There were 12,689 farms with less than 0.5 hectares counted in the 1970 census, compared to 12,441 in 1960. The 1960 census did not tabulate the area included in these very small farms. In 1970, this group of farms included a total of 1,372 hectares, an average of 0.1 hectares per farm. Most of these farms are small plots used for family subsistence. Some of these farmers are employed in other work, either as laborers on large farms or in off-farm occupations. More information is needed on this group of microfarms to understand their role in the rural and urban work forces.

The most useful classification of farms for a sector analysis would take income potential of the farm units into account. Income potential is related to size of farm but also depends on other factors such as land quality and location. Unfortunately, the only data available are from the census and classify farms by size. For this study, farms have been

1. Dirección General de Planificación y Administración de la Presidencia, Evaluación Preliminar de los Recursos Agro-Físicos de la República de Panamá, 1971.

TABLE 3.3. • NUMBER AND SIZE OF FARMS, 1960 AND 1970

Hectares	1960				1970			
	Farms		Area		Farms		Area	
	No.	%	Ha	%	No.	%	Ha	%
Less than 0.5[a]	12,441	--	n.a.	--	12,689	--	1,372	--
0.5 - 4.9	43,692	45.8	95,655	5.3	41,307	45.5	75,110	3.7
5.0 - 49.9	45,021	47.1	664,622	36.8	41,145	45.2	662,019	32.8
50.0 - 499.9	6,568	6.9	674,420	37.3	8,200	9.0	838,460	41.5
500 and More	224	0.2	371,755	20.6	290	0.3	443,779	22.0
Subtotal, 0.5 Ha & Larger	95,505	100.0	1,806,452	100.0	90,942	100.0	2,019,368	100.0
Total	107,946	--	--	--	103,631	--	2,020,740	--

Source: Segundo y Tercer Censo Agropecuario. 1970 data are preliminary.

[a]No information on land use by these microfarms was reported in the 1960 census nor in the preliminary results of the 1970 census.

grouped into the following four size classes: 0.5–4.9 hectares, 5.0–49.9 hectares, 50.0–499.9 hectares, and 500 hectares and over. In general, farms in the smallest category have insufficient land to provide reasonable levels of living for the farm families. At the other extreme, the largest farms could be termed "multifamily" in the sense that they have enough land to provide adequate incomes for more than a single family. The intermediate farms have potential as economic family-farm units, depending on land quality, location, level of technology, and cropping patterns. While the classification used is based on a rather arbitrary size criterion, the required information is not available for a more refined analysis.

In 1970, the largest number of farms was in the 0.5 to 4.9 hectare size class. This class contained more than 45% of the farms but less than 4% of the land area in farms. The 5.0 to 49.9 hectare size class also contained 45% of the farms but accounted for 33% of the total farmland. Taken together, these two small-farm size classes included 90% of the farms but only about 37% of the farmland.

Large farms in the 50.0 to 499.9 hectare size class accounted for 9% of the total farms and over 40% of the land area in farms. Only 0.3% of the farms were 500 hectares or larger; yet, these included 22% of the total farmland. Taken together, the two large-farm size classes contained about 10% of the farms but more than 63% of the land area in farms. Between 1960 and 1970, the number of farms in the two smaller size groups decreased somewhat. Increases occurred in the two large-farm groups. As a result, large farms accounted for a greater proportion of farmland in 1970 than in 1960.

These data on farm size distribution suggest that the question of what is the optimal distribution of land should be raised. Proponents of land reform will argue that little can be done for the poverty of small farmers as long as they have small parcels of land. Opponents will stress the high proportion of production marketed by large farms and the possible negative impact of land redistribution on agricultural output and investment.

As an alternative to redistribution of existing land, the government could choose to resettle landless laborers and small farmers on new lands. Much of the unused land is publicly owned. Road construction, including the project to close the Darien Gap, is increasing the new land available for settlement. A coherent agricultural development strategy in Panama is unlikely to include only one of the alternative approaches to land redistribution and settlement. Rather, the need is to clarify the costs and benefits of each alternative and to develop an integrated approach to agrarian policy that would blend different programs to best accomplish overall output and welfare objectives.

The process of land redistribution that took place between 1960 and 1970 appeared to follow a pattern. The number of small farms decreased somewhat as farmers with insufficient land migrated to the urban areas. Other small farmers relocated in newly opened areas. A small increase occurred in the number of farms with 50.0 hectares or more. These changes are continuing; they represent the classic process by which small farmers move out and their lands are consolidated by other farmers into larger units.

LAND TENANCY

Farms are operated under three main types of tenancy situations (farmed with title, rented, and farmed without title). About 70% of all farms are operated without title (Table 3.4). Lack of title is especially prevalent in the small-farm size classes. Over 73% of the farms in the 0.5 to 49.9 hectare size classes are farmed without title. Conversely, nearly 90% of the farmers with 500 or more hectares have title to their land. In the 50.0 to 499.9 hectare size class, slightly over half the farmers do not have title. In terms of land area, 990,020 hectares are farmed with title while 903,117 are farmed without. The remaining 202,338 hectares are rented.

The large number of farmers who do not have legal title to their land has important implications for agricultural development programs. Lack of title creates a serious barrier for credit and technical assistance programs directed to these farmers. This long-standing barrier has received some attention from the government, but an intensive land-titling program has not yet been undertaken. The magnitude of the title problem has been increasing. Between 1960 and 1970, the number of farmers without title to their land increased by 19%, and the area farmed on this precarious basis rose by more than 30%. It is estimated that about two-thirds of the land farmed without title actually is owned by the government, while the remainder is owned privately.

Responsibility for land titling was placed with the Agrarian Reform Commission created by the 1962 Agrarian Reform Law. The commission began to issue land titles in 1963. By the end of 1972, a total of 7,883 titles involving 129,416 hectares of land had been issued.[2] Although half of all titles issued since 1963 were given out in 1971–72, the commission has not been able to even keep pace with the formation of new farms.

UTILIZATION OF LAND BY FARM SIZE

Seventy percent of the land on farms in the 0.5 to 4.9 hectare size class was used for crop production in 1970 (Table 3.5). If fallow land is included, cropland accounted for more than three-fourths of the

2. Comisión de Reforma Agraria, Compendio Estadístico, 1963–1971 and Memoria, 1972.

TABLE 3.4. ● LAND TENANCY BY SIZE OF FARM, 1970

Farm Size Class (ha)	Total		With Title[a]		Rented[b]		Without Title	
	Farms	Area	Farms	Area	Farms	Area	Farms	Area
0.5 - 4.9	41,307	75,110	4,751	8,985	5,913	10,567	30,643	55,558
5.0 - 49.9	41,145	662,019	9,221	174,399	2,444	34,573	29,480	453,047
50.0 - 499.9	8,200	838,460	3,908	479,321	296	30,967	3,996	328,172
500 and More	290	443,779	239	327,315	19	126,231	32	66,340
Total	90,942	2,019,368	18,119	990,020	8,672	202,338	64,151	903,117

Source: Tercer Censo Agropecuario, Cifras Preliminares.

[a]Includes mixed tenancy if farmers owned some land.

[b]Includes farms with some land rented and some farmed without title.

TABLE 3.5. ● USE OF LAND BY FARM SIZE, 1970

Farm Size Class	Total (ha)	Annual (ha)	Crops (%)	Perennial (ha)	Crops (%)	Fallow Ha	Fallow %
0.5 - 4.9	75,110	36,305	48.3	16,396	21.8	6,434	8.6
5.0 - 49.9	662,019	91,283	13.8	47,024	7.1	113,028	17.1
50.0 - 499.9	838,460	54,566	6.5	20,504	2.5	69,536	8.3
500 and More	443,779	16,856	3.8	16,371	3.7	21,989	4.9
Total	2,019,368	199,010	9.9	100,294	5.0	210,987	10.4

Farm Size Class	Improved Pasture Ha	Improved Pasture %	Natural Pasture Ha	Natural Pasture %	Others Ha	Others %
0.5 - 4.9	4,787	6.4	3,042	4.1	8,146	10.8
5.0 - 49.9	226,847	34.3	56,976	8.6	126,861	19.1
50.0 - 499.9	482,960	57.6	76,270	9.1	134,625	16.0
500 and More	224,120	50.5	36,814	8.3	127,629	28.8
Total	738,714	46.5	173,102	8.5	397,261	19.7

Source: Tercer Censo Agropecuario, Cifras Preliminares.

total land area of this small-farm class. Only about 10% of the land of these small farmers is used for pasture.

In sharp contrast, farmers with 500 and more hectares per farm used less than 10% of their land for crops in 1970. Even when fallow land is included, cropland accounted for only about 12% of the land area for this large-farm size class. Pasture is the most important use of land for farmers in this group, occupying about 60% of the land area.

In the 50.0 to 499.9 hectare size class, pasture accounted for two-thirds of the land in farms. These farmers also used less than 10% of their land for crops. When fallow land is included, cropland rose to 17% of the total area. Crops occupied 20% of the land in the 5.0 to 49.9 hectare size class. Another 17% of land was fallow in this group, making cropland equal to 37% of the total area. Pastureland in this size class amounted to 43% of the land in farms.

In overall terms, a strong tendency exists for small farmers to use more of their land for crops than large farmers. A much greater proportion of land in large farms is used for pastures, a pattern which is not unexpected. Very small farmers use their land intensively in order to survive. Farmers that have more land but are still small continue to emphasize crop production. This latter group, however, leaves more land fallow and uses pasture to restore soil fertility levels. Large farms frequently are held for capital appreciation and use only a small proportion of their land for crops, devoting most of their land to extensive livestock production.

SALES OF PRODUCTS BY FARM SIZE

The most salient fact about sales of farm products is that 49,196 farms (47% of the total) reported no sales in 1970 (Table 3.6). For farms of 0.5 hectares or larger, the proportion without sales was 43%. The farms without sales are mostly subsistence units producing only for family consumption. This group of farms will be by far the most difficult target group to reach with modernization programs.

Another 27,752 farms reported sales of B/100 or less in 1970. Most of these farms have 50.0 hectares of land or less. Nevertheless, 40% of farms in the 50.0 to 499.9 hectare size class reported sales of B/100 or less.

At the other end of the spectrum, 1,328 farms sold products valued at B/5,000 or more in 1970. Another 9,173 farms had sales between B/500 and B/4,999 each.[3] Taken together, these two groups included only 11% of the farms. The proportion of the total value of off-farm sales made by these two groups cannot be precisely determined from available data, but it is certainly two-thirds and more likely about 80%

---

3. These data are preliminary. Revised data show fewer small farms with sales above B/500. No revised data by province had been released in time for inclusion here.

TABLE 3.6. • VALUE OF SALES BY FARM SIZE, 1970

Farm Size Class (ha)	Number of Farms	Number of Farms with No Sales	Number of Farms with Sales between:			
			B/1-99	B/100-499	B/500-4,999	B/5,000 and more
Less than 0.5	12,689	10,609	1,717	300	52	11
0.5 - 4.9	41,307	21,728	13,320	5,068	1,155	36
5.0 - 49.9	41,145	14,527	11,806	9,320	5,204	288
50.0 - 499.9	8,200	2,266	906	1,483	2,732	813
500 and More	290	66	3	11	30	180
Total	103,631	49,196	27,752	18,882	9,173	1,328

Source: Tercer Censo Agropecuario, Cifras Preliminares.

Note: These data are preliminary. The revised data published after this report was prepared show fewer small farms with sales of B/500 or more and no farms of 0.5 hectares or less with sales greater than B/500.

TABLE 3.7. ● SIZE DISTRIBUTION OF FARM SALES BY PROVINCE, 1970–71

| Province | Number of Farms with Sales | Number of Farms with Sales between: | | | | Number of Farms with No Sales |
		B/1-99	B/100-499	B/500-4,999	B/5,000 and more	
Bocas del Toro	591	229	199	142	21	334
Cocle	7,602	4,379	2,138	897	188	7,701
Colon	3,578	1,499	1,392	629	58	2,206
Chiriqui	9,691	4,093	3,198	1,939	461	9,821
Darien	1,093	298	466	313	16	198
Herrera	5,854	2,971	1,602	1,153	128	4,895
Los Santos	7,708	3,542	2,061	1,895	210	4,718
Panama	6,508	3,493	2,038	847	130	8,334
Veraguas	11,810	7,248	3,088	1,358	116	10,989
Total	54,435	27,752	16,182	9,173	1,328	49,196

Source: Tercer Censo Agropecuario, Cifras Preliminares.

to 90%. The remaining groups, which had sales between B/100 and B/499 each, numbered 18,882 in 1970. Most of these farms are small but still produce a marketable surplus over the subsistence needs of the families operating them.

The distribution of farm sales by size class is also available on a province basis (Table 3.7).[4] Large numbers of farms with no sales or sales of B/100 or less are found in Cocle, Chiriqui, Herrera, Los Santos, Panama, and Veraguas provinces.

Another indication of the market participation of farms is given by the census classification of "farms producing principally for the market." The census defines this group as "farms selling 50 per cent or more of their output in the market." In 1970, 20,917 farms were classified in this group. The total area of farms in this classification was 610,786 hectares, less than one-third of the total land in farms. These farms were concentrated in Cocle, Colon, Chiriqui, Herrera, Los Santos, Panama, and Veraguas provinces. Almost three-fourths of these farmers did not have legal title to their farms.[5] Insufficient data are available to determine the overlap between the 20,917 farms selling more than half of their output and the 29,383 farms reporting sales of B/100 or more, but it can be safely assumed to be high.

Even though these sales figures are very low, they represent the only sources of income for many farm families. In 1970, a total of 56,105 farm families derived no income from any other sources. The remaining 47,526 farm families received some income from off-farm sources; of this latter group, 30,500 families reported income from off-farm work, either by the farmer or some member of his family.

In 1970, the gross value of agricultural output (in current prices) was B/222 million. An estimate from an International Labor Organization (ILO) study placed the gross value of output of farms between 0.5 and 4.9 hectares at B/18 million.[6] The composition of the output of small farms was the following:

Annual crops	B/5.5 million
Permanent crops	B/9.0 million
Livestock and animal products	B/3.5 million
Total	B/18.0 million

Thus this group of small farms produced 8% of the total output on slightly less than 4% of the land in farms.

4. Table 3.7 is based on the total of 103,631 farms in 1970, including farms of less than 0.5 ha. Data on farm size by province for 1970 had not yet been published when this report was written.

5. All data from Tercer Censo Agropecuario, Cifras Preliminares.

6. ILO, La Situación y Perspectivas del Empleo en Panamá, Vol. 2 (January 1973), pp. iv–11.

LEVEL OF TECHNOLOGY

Little data on technology has been published from the 1970 census. Preliminary data did show that only 27,200 farms used animal or mechanical power in farming operations. Geographic distribution of these farms is similar to those classified as producing principally for the market, but these groups are not necessarily the same. The data show that three-fourths of the farms selling more than half of their output used only human labor for production. A total of 75,331 of the 90,942 farms of 0.5 hectares or more reported that in 1970 all the labor used on the farm was provided by the farmer and his family. On another 9,100 farms, family labor represented an important part but not all of the labor supply; 5,950 farms were operated primarily with hired labor. Only 2,607 farms (less than 3% of total farms) reported receiving technical assistance in 1970–71, while credit was used by 10,427 farms. No data on use of fertilizer, improved seed, irrigation, etc., have been reported, but it is obviously extremely limited.

The ILO study contained estimates of technological levels for the principal annual and permanent crops for 1970–71 (Table 3.8).[7] The classification was based on the relationship between yields per hectare and size and organization of the farms. In general, modern technology (i.e., high yields) was associated with large farms and those organized for commercial production. It was estimated that more than half the area of the principal annual crops was produced under traditional, low-yield technology. In contrast, less than one-fourth of the permanent crops was produced using traditional methods of cultivation.

Data on rice yields are available for small and large farms. Average yields in 1971–72 were estimated at 20.0 quintals per hectare for small farms versus 51.2 quintals per hectare for large farms; the overall national average yield was 31.5 quintals per hectare.[8]

These estimates suggest a large scope for programs designed to improve yields on traditional farms, especially for annual crops. Such programs would increase production by raising average yields and would help to increase the income of small farms, thereby improving income distribution in the agricultural sector. Since higher yields are already being achieved on the larger farms, new technology is available for diffusion to the traditional farmers; the challenge lies in designing credit and technical assistance programs that would make it possible for small farmers to utilize yield-increasing technology.

7. ILO, 1973, pp. iv–11.
8. Dirección de Estadística y Censo, Estadística Panamá, Información Agropecuaria, Series "H," No. 1, p. 5.

TABLE 3.8. • LEVEL OF TECHNOLOGY FOR PRINCIPAL CROPS, 1970–71

Crops	Traditional	Semimodern	Modern	Total
		(thousands of hectares)		
Annual Crops				
Rice	49.4	28.2	18.5	96.1
Corn	44.5	16.0	8.8	69.3
Beans	11.6	4.2	2.3	18.1
Sugarcane	6.9	8.5	8.6	24.0
Subtotal	112.4	56.9	38.2	207.5
(Percent)	(54.2)	(27.4)	(18.4)	(100.0)
Permanent Crops				
Coffee	7.4	14.5	--	21.9
Banana	5.8	6.2	24.2	36.2
Plantain	2.2	7.2	1.8	11.2
Subtotal	15.4	27.9	26.0	69.3
(Percent)	(22.2)	(40.3)	(37.5)	(100.0)
Total	127.8	84.8	64.8	276.8
(Percent)	(46.2)	(30.6)	(23.2)	(100.0)

Source: ILO, 1973.

AGRICULTURAL INPUTS

Almost all modern inputs used in agricultural production are imported, including fertilizers, pesticides and herbicides, seeds, machinery, and feedstuffs.

Fertilizer imports tripled between 1960 and 1970 (Table 3.9). Most fertilizer is imported as nitrogen or mixed forms. It is estimated that 80% to 90% of nitrogen fertilizer is used for banana production with the remainder mostly used for rice. The main uses for mixed fertilizer are rice, sugarcane, and citrus fruits.

Although rice and corn seed are produced, imports of seed for grain production have increased substantially. Supplying national needs for these grains through domestic production will require investments in seed processing and storage facilities as well as expanded research programs to develop and test improved varieties.

Imports of herbicides and pesticides increased from B/347,000 in 1960 to B/2.2 million in 1970. Between 1960 and 1970, the value of imports of tractors and agricultural machinery increased from B/400,000 to more than B/4 million. Use of these modern inputs tends to be concentrated in the relatively few large, mechanized farms.

UNDEREMPLOYMENT IN THE AGRICULTURAL SECTOR

In 1970, the 158,000 workers in the agricultural labor force were classified as follows:

Farmers (55%)	87,000
Family workers (24%)	38,000
Hired workers (21%)	33,000
Total	158,000[9]

Hired labor was used on nearly 17% of farms in 1970. Those remaining were operated by labor provided solely by the farmer and his family.

The 1970 Census of Agriculture counted a total population of 575,924 in the rural sector. Using an average family size of 5.5, the agricultural population was distributed by farm size approximately as follows:

FARM SIZE CLASS (HECTARES)	POPULATION
0.0– 0.5	72,000
0.5– 4.9	225,000
5.0– 49.9	224,000
50.0–499.9	45,000
500 and more	15,000

9. This figure comes from the 1970 employment data. It includes workers 15 years old or older and excludes the Indian population.

TABLE 3.9. ● **FERTILIZER IMPORTS, 1960–70**

Year	Total	Type of Fertilizer			
		Nitrogen	Phosphate	Potassium	Mixed
			(metric tons)		
1960	15,325	11,352	527	286	3,160
1961	19,311	14,905	685	457	3,264
1962	16,963	11,649	1,577	460	3,274
1963	16,965	15,505	1,228	578	2,654
1964	23,745	19,312	1,016	509	2,908
1965	30,622	22,847	1,658	1,029	5,089
1966	23,277	15,505	1,910	161	8,701
1967	33,263	15,732	1,347	600	15,584
1968	40,317	19,115	738	373	20,046
1969	46,990	24,305	315	804	21,565
1970	47,153	24,780	2,070	131	20,176

Source: Nancy Fong, Insumos Agropecuarios, February 1972.

Using an average figure of 1.5 economically active workers per farm family, the farm family labor force can be allocated to farm size as follows:

FARM SIZE CLASS (HECTARES)	FARM FAMILY WORKERS	HECTARES PER FARM FAMILY WORKER
0.0– 0.5	20,000	0.1
0.5– 4.9	63,000	1.2
5.0– 49.9	62,500	10.6
50.0–499.9	12,000	69.6
500 and more	500	887.5

Clearly, family workers on farms in some size classes are unlikely to be fully employed. While some of this excess labor is utilized as hired labor on large farms and in off-farm employment, substantial underutilization surely remains.

Results of the ILO study indicated that 23.6% of the available work time of the agricultural labor force was not required for production in 1970 (Table 3.10). The study then projected underemployment to 1980 based on assumptions about demand, yields, degree of mechanization, and growth in the agricultural labor force.

Total labor requirements for the 1970–71 agricultural year were estimated, taking into account land in crops and in pastures, number of livestock, and level of technology. Seasonal differences in requirements were not considered; labor scarcities could occur in some regions in peak periods along with substantial underemployment in other periods. The study concluded that 37 million man-days were required for production in 1970–71.

Available labor time for 1970–71 was estimated on the basis of an agricultural work force of 183,000 persons. This labor force definition includes all workers ten years old or older and the Indian population. Assuming 265 working days per year resulted in total available labor time of 48.4 million man-days.

Underemployment was defined as the percentage by which available labor time exceeded labor requirements (23.6% in 1970–71). This figure provides some indication of the amount of labor that could be withdrawn from the agricultural sector without reducing production and without substituting other inputs; it represents the equivalent of about 44,000 full-time workers.[10] It should be emphasized that this calculation is based on the annual average labor requirements. Rapid withdrawal of this number of workers probably would create serious labor shortages in periods of peak seasonal requirements in some areas.

10. Compare this conclusion to the projection in Chapter 1 that 43,000 male workers will migrate from farm to urban occupations between 1970 and 1980.

TABLE 3.10. • UNDEREMPLOYMENT OF THE AVAILABLE AGRICULTURAL LABOR FORCE, 1970 AND PROJECTIONS TO 1980

Labor	1970-71	1980 No increase in mechanization		Increased mechanization	
		A[a]	B[b]	A[a]	B[b]
Total Labor Requirements (millions of man-days)	37.0	47.0	43.6	43.5	40.4
Available Labor Time[c] (millions of man-days)	48.4				
No increase in labor time		48.4	48.4	48.4	48.4
0.6% increase per year in labor time		51.4	51.4	51.4	51.4
Underemployment of the Agricultural Labor Force (%)	23.6				
No increase in labor time		2.9	9.9	10.1	16.5
0.6% increase per year in labor time		88.6	15.2	15.4	21.4

Source: ILO, 1973, p. iv-9.

[a] Yields equal to the 1960-70 average.

[b] Higher yields for rice, corn, beans, and sugar.

[c] Assumes 265 working days per worker; based on a work force of 183,000 persons using the work force definition that includes all workers ten years old or older and includes the Indian population.

Underemployment in 1980 was analyzed on the basis of projected internal and export demand and alternative assumptions about labor force changes and the degree of mechanization. The results of the 1980 projections are given in Table 3.10. The most favorable situation in terms of underemployment in 1980 involves the following assumptions: (1) the agricultural labor force does not grow, (2) yields do not increase, and (3) mechanization does not increase. If all these assumptions were fulfilled, underemployment in agriculture would nearly disappear by 1980. Conversely, if the agricultural labor force continues to grow at the current level of 0.6% per year, yields increase, and more mechanization takes place, underemployment will remain at about the same level in 1980 as in 1970.

It may be surprising that increases in yields (shown by the differences in columns A and B in Table 3.10) appear to cause higher rates of underemployment. Other things being equal, higher yields usually require more labor per unit of land, although the quantity of labor per unit of output falls. In the ILO analysis, the alternative yield assumptions involve a trade-off between more land at lower yields and less land at higher yields to produce an output equal to the projected demand. In terms of labor requirements, the changes due to reduced area outweigh those due to higher yields; hence, less total labor is required to produce the given output.

The importance of the ILO study does not lie in the specific estimate of underemployment in 1970 nor in the alternative projections for 1980. The 1970 estimate, while based on careful and detailed analysis, contains many arbitrary assumptions. The 1980 projections are not a forecast of what is likely to happen that year but an indication of the impact that several factors will tend to have on labor utilization in agriculture.

The study suggests that one of the most critical factors affecting underemployment in agriculture is the change that takes place in the size of the labor force. If the labor force does not increase, significant improvement in its utilization can be expected. An actual decline in the absolute size of the agricultural labor force would improve labor productivity even more. What will actually happen depends on the relative strength of the "pull" that is exerted by job opportunities in urban areas and the "push" of the low-income levels in the rural sector. As shown in Chapters 1 and 2, Panama is likely to reach the point in the mid-1970s where the agricultural labor force reaches its maximum in absolute terms and begins to decline.

Mechanization increases output per worker but reduces the labor force required for a given area of production. It has a favorable impact on the productivity and income of workers employed and an unfavorable effect on workers who lose their jobs unless alternative employment is available to the displaced workers. The pure mechanization effect can be seen in Table 3.10 by comparing the A columns (or the B columns) on the two sides of the 1980 part of the table. Increased mechanization is consistent with reduced underemployment only if the agricultural labor force remains constant or declines.

Mechanization in agriculture is encouraged by several factors, one of which is the profitability of large-scale mechanized production of crops such as rice, sugar, and bananas. Another is the difficulty in obtaining labor to meet peak requirements in some areas. A third is the availability of credit from government and private sources for machinery purchases. Some indication of the impact that mechanization has on productivity and income per worker is indicated by the comparison of a daily wage rate of B/1 to B/2 for hand laborers, compared to B/4 to B/5 for tractor operators.

Mechanization alone undoubtedly will worsen income distribution in agriculture because owners and full-time skilled workers on large farms will benefit more in relation to small traditional farmers producing largely for subsistence purposes. In contrast, yield-increasing technology can benefit small farmers as well as large ones.

The effect of yield increases is shown by comparing column A with column B in each of the two sides of the 1980 part of Table 3.10. In these two comparisons, underemployment is higher in column B than in A due to the decrease in area required to produce the specified quantities demanded, even though more labor per hectare is needed at the higher yields. Given the demand limitations, the employment impact of decreased area in production outweighs the favorable effects of yield-increasing technology. If 1980 output were not assumed to be fixed so that cropping areas could be maintained or increased, the use of chemical and biological technology to raise yields would mean more employment rather than less and a higher growth rate in agricultural output.

The relative emphasis on mechanization and yield-increasing technology should be considered carefully. Both have their role. Since rural-urban migration will apparently keep the growth of the agricultural labor force to a low (if not zero or negative) level, mechanization will be needed on the growing number of larger, modern farm units. At the same time, chemical and biological technology to increase yields should be made available to small traditional farmers to raise their productivity and absorb underemployed labor. Without this dual approach, output gains will intensify rather than diminish income inequality in the agricultural sector.

FORESTRY RESOURCES

The forestry resources in the Darien region, between the Canal Zone and Colombia, are the base for a potentially important industry.[11]

11. Much of the material in this section is based on a study by Greenacres, Inc., Forests of the Republic of Panama, Panama, 1963. Although this study is somewhat outdated, the forestry industry has changed very little since 1963.

Excluding San Blas, 27,207 square kilometers, or approximately 36% of Panama's total land area, comprise this region. Forests with an estimated 77 billion board feet of standing timber cover about 80% of the Darien region.

It is estimated that between 7,000 and 8,000 hectares of this forest are being converted to agricultural or urban use each year. Some large cattle farms are located at the edge of the forest near Panama City, but shifting subsistence agriculture is practiced in much of the Darien region. There is very little cultivation of tree crops such as coconuts, African oil palm, cacao, or rubber. Some of the indigenous Indian population have developed a fallow system of agriculture along the waterways where alluvial soil is found in relatively flat areas. Under this system, the land is farmed a few years and then allowed to return to brush for five to ten years before it is farmed again. The system has little impact on the surrounding forest.

A small forest products industry produces plywood and lumber for domestic markets. A small amount of cedar and mahogany logs are exported. The existing industry uses only 15% of the approximately 120 tree species believed to have some commercial value.

Little incentive exists to make much additional investment in the forestry industry on the basis of the present or foreseen domestic market. Expansion of the forestry products industry depends on the ability to compete in international markets. International competition is presently difficult due to the (1) import restrictions of other countries, (2) lack of roads in the Darien region, (3) lack of deep-water port facilities on the Pacific coast of the Darien region, (4) high conference sea freight rates on logs and lumber products, and (5) low price of the lumber from many species that are abundant.

Nearly all Panama's forest volume is in hardwood species. Europe and Japan are the main importers of hardwood logs and lumber; hardwood for the United States accounts for only a small percentage of total U.S. lumber imports. Hardwood logs are used by Japan to supply its rotary-peeling plywood industry; most of these come from East Asia. Logs for the sliced-face veneer industry are Europe's most important hardwood import. Both Asia and Africa are important sources of tropical hardwoods for Europe.

Hardwood logs are the main product that Panama might sell to Japan. The delivered prices of logs would not be competitive, however, unless nonconference sea freight rates substantially below the quoted conference rates can be developed. Eventually, it may be possible for Panama to sell some veneer products to Japan. The development of this market would require the interest and close cooperation of the large Japanese trading companies.

Hardwood logs and matching lumber are about the only wood products that Panama might sell to Europe. The potential European market for core stock veneer is very limited because of the thin sizes of plywood used. It may eventually be possible to sell some rotary-peeled plywood of utility sheet grade in the European market, much of which would be used for industrial packaging. The development of this market would require the close cooperation of large European companies using utility plywood.

Potential markets for hardwood products in the United States are for industrial grade hardwood lumber, hardwood plywood, special veneers, and cheap core stock veneers. Panama's ability to capture part of these markets will depend on its ability to supply large quantities of uniform quality product at competitive prices.

Panama presently imports large amounts of paper products of which newsprint, kraft, and wrapping papers are the most important. Some of these paper products are consumed within Panama, but much of the container board and wrapping paper is used in packaging export items, especially bananas. Growth in domestic demand for most paper products will depend primarily on the rate of population growth.

The demand for kraft paper and corrugated paper containers will be influenced by the development of export industries and changes in packaging techniques. It is technically feasible to make kraft paper and container board from some of the hardwoods. Growth of the pulp and paper industry will be tied closely to development of the sawmills and plywood plants that provide pulp and paper raw materials as residuals of their operations.

About 40% of the standing timber in the Darien region is quipo (similar to balsa), which presently has very limited commercial value. Espave (wild cashew) accounts for nearly 9% of the timber volume. It can be used for fancy panel and utility plywood, core stock veneer, and molding. Spanish cedar accounts for about 5.5% of the timber volume; it can be used for cigar boxes and specialty panel plywood. There are an estimated 3.8 billion board feet of Spanish walnut (cativo) in the Darien region. Cativo is a low-price wood that can be used as core stock veneer, utility plywood, and face veneers. Most of the readily accessible riverbank stands of nearly pure Spanish walnut have been logged heavily. About 85% of the existing volume of Spanish walnut is intermixed with quipo at low elevations. Mahogany (caoba) is often found as scattered individual trees in small groups; it has been cut for many years and has been nearly eliminated in all but the most inaccessible areas.

The average volume of lumber per hectare in the forests is about equal to that in the dipterocarp forests of the Far East. However, if quipo is not considered, the average volume per hectare falls below that of most commercially exploited dipterocarp forests. The average volume per tree is about one-half that of trees in the dipterocarp forests of the Far East.

In summary, commercial development of the Darien region forest is unlikely to take place until the Darien Highway has been completed, port facilities on the region's Pacific coast are improved, and a system of feeder roads is developed. It seems unlikely that these infrastructure changes will be completed prior to 1980–85. Large-scale commercial development of Panama's forests, therefore, is unlikely to start much before the mid-1980s and is more probable during the early 1990s. If Panama is to maximize the long-run returns from its forest resources, however, an enforceable national forest policy will be needed before the Darien Highway is completed. As a minimum, this policy should assure that commercially valuable forests are not cut and burned on a large-scale basis to establish farms as the Darien Highway is constructed. Protection of the forests can be accomplished by establishing national forests and controlling their use with cutting licenses that limit the way forests are cut and renewed.

SUMMARY AND IMPLICATIONS

Panama's agricultural sector exhibits an economic structure and characteristics that result in serious underemployment of farm labor and highly unequal distribution of agricultural income. Most of the increases in farms between 1960 and 1970 were due to increase in pastureland. More than three-fourths of the increase in pastureland that took place during this period occurred on farms of 50 hectares or larger; most of these farms employ extensive methods of livestock production. The increase in agricultural output has not been general for all types and sizes of farms. The largest increases have occurred in rice, sugar, bananas, and beef on larger farms that utilize mechanized techniques of production.

The agricultural sector also shows a sharp duality in its structure. Most of the farms are small and produce rice, corn, and beans under traditional technology, largely for home consumption. Little credit and purchased inputs are used, production is based almost entirely on human labor, and family labor is the principal input used for production. A few larger farms are highly mechanized and use modern inputs for production. Most of these farms produce rice and perennial tree crops. The large farms that are not highly mechanized usually produce cattle, using extensive technology.

The poverty of small farmers producing cereal crops by hand labor for home consumption is one of the most pressing agricultural problems. These small farms have depleted soils and low yields. The farmers use no credit and receive no technical assistance. Lack of legal title is prevalent among small farmers, leading to insecurity of tenure and an inability to use land as a basis for obtaining credit. Awarding land titles is a prerequisite to any programs designed to reach small farmers, but titles alone will do little to raise productivity and incomes of small subsistence farmers.

Substantial migration from rural areas has occurred. Most of this migration represents small farmers and their families seeking a better life in urban locations. Other small farmers have moved to new agricultural areas seeking more and better land. Many of these migrants have found themselves unemployed or underemployed in minor trades or services in the cities or back in subsistence agriculture.

Migration into the Darien region is expected to increase during the seventies. Commercial development of the Darien region forest is unlikely to take place before the Darien Highway is completed and a system of feeder roads developed. Meanwhile, a national forest policy will be needed to assure that commercially valuable forests are not destroyed as farming in the region increases.

CHAPTER FOUR

SUPPLY AND DEMAND PROJECTIONS FOR AGRICULTURAL PRODUCTS

THIS CHAPTER concentrates on supply and demand projections for livestock products, basic grains, fruits, sugar, vegetables, and forestry products. The relative importance of the various food products in the Panamanian diet, in terms of kilograms consumed annually per capita in 1970, is shown in Table 4.1. This ranking of foods illustrates the importance of fruits, especially bananas and oranges. From a nutritional viewpoint, however, one might assert that rice and beef are the most important food commodities produced. Average daily intake in 1970 was 2,475 calories, slightly below the FAO recommended minimum level of 2,550. Protein intake was 59.6 grams (Table 4.2) with cereals being the main source of both calories and protein. Rice alone provides about 25% of the average daily calorie intake and about 20% of the protein intake. Meats are the second most important source of protein, accounting for over 24% of the average daily protein intake in 1970; animal proteins (meat, eggs, and milk) accounted for nearly 35% of the total protein intake.

Most of the supply and demand projections presented in this chapter assume that past food balances will continue. However, food consumption habits undoubtedly will change as relative prices change, as incomes increase, and as the urban population continues to grow; but such changes are expected to be gradual. Production patterns, on the other hand, could change quite rapidly, depending on developments in the world market, the speed with which the Darien region is opened, and the success of various government programs. As a result, long-run supply projections are likely to be less accurate than long-run demand projections.

TABLE 4.1. ● ANNUAL PER CAPITA CONSUMPTION OF MAJOR FOODS

Rank	Product	Kg/Capita/Yr	Relative Importance (%)
1	Fruits	152.4	32.8
2	Cereals	106.9	23.0
3	Milk	39.1	8.4
4	Root Crops	36.7	7.9
5	Meat	35.5	7.6
6	Sugar	28.2	6.1
7	Vegetables	25.8	5.5
8	Beans	13.6	2.9
9	Fats and Oils	11.4	2.5
10	Fish and Seafood	10.8	2.3
11	Eggs	4.1	1.0
	Total	464.5	100.0

Source: Dirección de Estadística y Censo, Hojas de Balances de Alimentos: Años 1960 a 1970, Panamá, 1971.

GRAINS

Rice and corn are the major food grains in the diet;[1] dry beans also are relatively important. The small grains (wheat, barley, and oats) are not produced in any significant quantities. Grain sorghum and soybeans have been tried on a limited scale, but they are not yet established as economically significant crops.

Rice is the major grain crop in most provinces and the dominant crop in the large, mechanized farming areas such as Chiriqui and Cocle. In most areas, rainfall is ample and irrigation is not required for rice production. By following the early fall harvest with a winter ratoon,

1. Much of the material in this section is from Richard Phillips, Needs and Opportunities for Improved Grain Marketing in Panama during the Decade Ahead, Report 28, Food and Feed Grain Institute, Kansas State University, Manhattan, October 1971.

TABLE 4.2. ● **DAILY CONSUMPTION OF CALORIES, PROTEINS, AND FATS, 1970**

Product	Proteins		Calories		Fats	
	Grams	%	Units	%	Grams	%
Cereals	23.0	38.7	1,052	42.5	4.6	7.8
Meats	14.4	24.2	164	6.6	11.2	19.0
Fish and Seafood	5.5	9.2	39	1.6	1.7	2.9
Milk Products	5.2	8.7	116	4.7	4.7	8.0
Beans	4.6	7.7	86	3.5	2.4	4.1
Fruits	2.7	4.5	220	8.9	1.3	2.2
Root Crops	1.3	2.2	102	4.1	0.1	0.2
Eggs	1.2	2.0	16	0.6	1.2	2.0
Vegetables	0.8	1.3	17	0.7	0.1	0.2
Sugar	0.4	0.7	287	11.6	1.0	1.7
Fats and Oils	--	--	267	10.8	30.2	51.2
Beverages	--	--	102	4.1	--	--
Others	0.5	0.8	7	0.3	0.4	0.7
Totals	59.6	100.0	2,475	100.0	58.9	100.0
Amount Supplied by Imported Foods	16.3	27.4	504	20.4	8.3	14.1[a]

Source: Hojas de Balances de Alimentos: Años 1960 a 1970.

[a]The relative importance of imported fats is underestimated due to the procedure used in estimating domestic production of fats and oils.

the more skilled farmers can produce two crops per year on the same land. Rice is harvested at relatively high moisture content and must be dried artificially prior to storage and milling.

Corn is grown throughout the country but has greatest relative importance in the central provinces, particularly Los Santos, Herrera, and Panama. About 55% of the corn harvest is used for human consumption. That remaining is used for livestock feed and seed on farms (about 35%) and as an ingredient for commercial poultry and livestock feeds (about 10%). Corn is harvested both in the fall (about 60%) and the spring (about 40%). There are large, mechanized corn producers; but compared to rice production, corn is relatively more popular among the small nonmechanized farmers.

Beans are primarily a spring crop (about 88% of the annual production), grown following the fall harvest of rice or corn. Most of the bean crop is produced by small farmers with little or no mechanization.

Rice production has increased steadily, from about 96,000 tons of rough rice in 1960 to over 136,000 tons in 1971. The increased production has kept pace with growing domestic demand, so that there has been little surplus for rice export and little need for rice imports. Corn production also increased over the same period but at a slower rate; corn imports have averaged about 2% of total consumption. The production of edible beans has not increased significantly, and imports have grown.

A large percentage of Panama's grain production is consumed on the farm. Of their 1969–70 crop, producers retained for on-farm consumption about 47.5% of the rice, 67% of the corn (26% for food and 41% for feed and seed), and 50% of the edible beans. The percentages of grains retained are expected to decline as total production increases and migration to urban areas continues.

Grain production plays a dominant role. The vast majority of farmers in all provinces produce rice; a large percentage of these same farmers also cultivate corn and edible beans. About 35% of the nation's cropland is devoted to rice production, 28.5% to corn production, and 5% to the production of edible beans.

Patterns of Rice Production

The reported total annual production of rice by province for the crop years 1960–61 through 1969–70 is shown in Table 4.3. Over the ten-year period, total production increased from 2,114,800 quintals to 3,643,000 quintals. Except for Los Santos, all provinces shared the increase in rice production, but the major increases have occurred in Chiriqui and Cocle provinces. Average annual increase in production was 81,681 quintals in Chiriqui and 40,709 quintals in Cocle. In 1970,

TABLE 4.3. ● **PRODUCTION OF RICE BY PROVINCE, 1960–70**

Year	Bocas del Toro	Chiriqui	Veraguas	Herrera	Los Santos	Cocle	Panama	Colon	Darien	Country Total
1960-61	4.2	523.4	657.5	223.7	285.9	157.3	184.0	36.4	42.4	2,114.8
1961-62	6.8	645.8	634.4	206.3	325.9	182.9	271.1	57.1	70.3	2,400.6
1962-63	6.1	639.7	606.0	250.8	313.6	217.5	255.7	59.8	69.3	2,418.5
1963-64	8.4	637.6	567.5	266.4	339.1	190.7	272.2	61.8	107.3	2,451.0
1964-65	17.9	677.5	689.3	357.4	394.5	199.6	285.0	82.8	111.8	2,815.8
1965-66	9.3	878.6	940.7	360.1	265.7	318.9	347.2	79.5	139.4	3,339.4
1966-67	9.0	767.2	814.2	289.1	287.3	276.8	408.6	78.8	157.0	3,088.0
1967-68	9.0	1,035.5	893.1	282.2	270.3	295.9	334.9	69.1	147.3	3,337.3
1969-70	6.8	1,368.5	761.0	260.1	281.9	559.9	223.1	57.6	125.0	3,643.0
Average	8.3	829.2	748.8	287.2	304.4	291.4	285.5	67.7	109.5	2,932.0
Percent	0.3	28.3	25.5	9.8	10.4	9.9	9.7	2.3	3.8	100.0

Source: Superficie, sembrada y producción de arroz, maíz y frijol, 1961–1970. Estadística Panameña: Información Agropecuaria, Panamá, 1971.

Chiriqui and Cocle accounted for over 52% of Panama's total rice production.

The greatest percentage increases in rice production have occurred in Cocle (256%), Darien (195%), and Chiriqui (161%). Rice production in these three provinces is dominated by large producers with fully mechanized operations. Their rice fields are relatively large, and most of the harvest is done with self-propelled crawler-track combines owned by custom operators.

In contrast, rice farms are smaller and less mechanized in Veraguas than in any other province. Land in this area has been cultivated for many years, and limited opportunities exist for expanding farm size. The fields are too small for harvesting by combine, and no suitable small-scale mechanical harvesters have been developed. Even in this area where population pressure on the land is great, labor is a limiting factor during planting and harvest. Farmers reportedly avoid some of the high-yielding strains and heavier seeding rates because of the scarcity of hand labor for harvest. The low-yield strategy keeps the cost of rice production per hectare relatively low but does make the cost per quintal very high in relation to production in mechanized areas. The labor scarcity problem of the small farm exists to a somewhat lesser extent in Herrera, Los Santos, Panama, and Colon provinces.

Rice is produced primarily for fall harvest, when weather conditions normally are most favorable. Plantings of first-crop rice continued to increase from 73,700 hectares in 1960–61 to 111,200 hectares in 1969–70, while plantings of the second crop remained relatively stable at about 15,000 hectares. During this period, the first crop represented 86.5% of total rice plantings. Normally, two crops of rice are not grown on the same land. However, some farmers have begun to grow a ratoon second crop by harvesting the first crop just ahead of the rains, so that the volunteer crop can be harvested in time for plowing and preparing the land for the first crop of the following year.

Grain yields have shown a consistent upward trend, which is more pronounced for rice than for corn or edible beans. It is also most pronounced in Chiriqui province, where the large, mechanized farms have taken greater advantage of advancing production technology.

During the 1960–70 period, rice yields averaged about 22 quintals of rough rice per hectare. Average yields in Chiriqui and Darien provinces are about 38% higher than the national average. Rice yields also are increasing more rapidly in these two provinces. Average yields are relatively good in Herrera, but the annual increase is much less rapid (about 0.4 quintals per hectare). The annual increase in yield is fairly rapid in Cocle (1.7 quintals per hectare), but the average yield is only about 20 quintals per hectare. For the most part, rice yields are increasing most rapidly in provinces where they already are high and increasing more slowly where yields are lower.

Patterns of Corn Production

The total annual 1960–70 production of corn by province is shown in Table 4.4. Over this period, corn production has increased from 1,295,500 to 1,929,300 quintals, an increase of one-half. Corn production has increased substantially in all nine provinces but most rapidly in Chiriqui and Veraguas. These provinces increased corn production by 80% and accounted for 45% of average total production during the ten-year period.

The area planted in corn has increased rather steadily in all provinces during the sixties. Considering the country as a whole, planting of the two corn crops has increased from 77,300 hectares in 1960–61 to 102,500 hectares in 1969–70, an average increase of about 2,900 hectares per year. Approximately one-third of the increase in area planted in corn has been in Veraguas province alone, with Chiriqui and Cocle together accounting for another one-third. When compared to area planted in rice, the area devoted to corn production is relatively more important in the central provinces of Los Santos, Panama, and Colon. For example, in 1969–70, the area planted in corn in Los Santos was 135% of that in rice, while in Chiriqui, the area planted in corn was only 68% of that in rice.

The average corn yields in Los Santos, Herrera, Chiriqui, and Darien are 15% to 25% above the national average of 17.5 quintals of shelled corn per hectare. With the exception of Herrera, yields in these provinces are increasing at an average annual rate of about 0.5 quintals per hectare, well above the national average. Yield trend in Herrera is slightly downward. The index of corn yields is below the national average in Veraguas, Bocas del Toro, Colon, Panama, and Cocle, with the yield trend varying from slightly downward to slightly upward in these four provinces.

One reason for the low corn yields is the large production of flint varieties because of the preference for them as human food. There seems to be great potential for increasing corn yields through the use of hybrid seed, increased fertilization, thicker planting, and other improved cultural practices.

Production cost disadvantage of the small farms in Veraguas province, when compared to the large farms in Chiriqui province, is less notable for corn than for rice. However, hand harvesting of corn generally is less costly than mechanical harvesting, and even if cornfields are large enough to harvest mechanically, custom operators are reluctant to invest in corn heads when they can keep their machines busy harvest-

TABLE 4.4. ● PRODUCTION OF CORN BY PROVINCE, 1960–70

Year	Bocas del Toro	Chiriqui	Veraguas	Herrera	Los Santos	Cocle	Panama	Colon	Darien	Country Total
1960-61	7.8	264.5	276.5	175.4	298.0	75.5	152.6	23.0	22.2	1,295.5
1961-62	3.9	422.7	312.3	178.6	305.6	93.9	208.6	47.6	59.6	1,632.8
1962-63	9.3	334.8	255.9	198.5	351.0	123.0	207.5	48.6	61.2	1,589.8
1963-64	8.8	469.6	332.2	174.5	311.0	85.9	156.1	60.0	74.1	1,672.2
1964-65	14.8	398.5	412.6	191.2	355.8	83.9	200.7	51.7	91.0	1,805.6
1965-66	6.9	444.7	396.6	169.8	366.2	115.8	200.5	44.0	115.6	1,860.1
1966-67	5.0	460.5	364.7	212.0	349.2	103.5	218.5	42.7	92.9	1,849.0
1967-68	111.0	513.7	419.4	170.5	315.0	140.0	252.2	43.7	93.9	1,959.5
1968-69	9.6	433.7	336.8	183.8	372.3	127.2	236.4	54.1	92.2	1,846.1
1969-70	9.6	475.8	441.2	201.0	338.2	120.4	204.3	50.9	87.9	1,929.3
Average	8.7	421.9	354.8	185.5	316.2	106.9	203.7	47.2	83.0	1,727.9
Percent	0.5	24.4	20.6	10.7	18.3	6.2	11.8	2.7	4.8	100.0

Source: Estadística Panameña: Información Agropecuaria.

ing rice. Consequently, many of the larger farmers still harvest corn by hand.

Pattern of Bean Production

Edible beans are produced throughout Panama, but production is concentrated in Chiriqui and Veraguas provinces (Table 4.5). Over the ten-year period from 1960–70, Veraguas accounted for 36% and Chiriqui for 29.6% of the production of edible beans. However, production in these two provinces, as well as for the country as a whole, has fluctuated widely from year to year and shows no significant trend through time. Total production reached peaks of 158,800 quintals in 1962–63 and 161,150 quintals in 1966–67 but averaged only 125,380 quintals over the ten-year period.

Even in mechanized production areas, edible beans represent a labor-intensive crop. Development of higher yielding strains, along with other cultural innovations, has not kept pace with technology for growing rice and corn. Consequently, bean production costs per quintal remain quite high, and farmers have found it more profitable to expand their production of rice and corn. The government's relative support prices have encouraged rice and corn production at the expense of edible bean production.

The area devoted to edible bean production is small compared to that devoted to rice and corn. The average annual decline in area planted in the two crops of edible beans has been 660 hectares. The biggest annual decline has been in Chiriqui (455 hectares), but the trend has been downward in nearly all provinces. Edible beans are predominantly a winter crop, following either rice or corn. Over the ten-year period, 81% of the total area devoted to edible beans was in second-crop plantings. Average bean yields during the 1960–70 period ranged from 5.6 quintals per hectare in Chiriqui province to 9.1 quintals in the province of Panama. The ten-year national average was 6.9 quintals per hectare.

Patterns of Grain Utilization

The supply-utilization table for rice, corn, and edible beans by province for the 1969–70 marketing year is shown in Table 4.6. The market demand figures represent the total demand for the province minus the reported volume of home consumption. Surplus or deficit for the province is obtained by subtracting the market demand from the marketings in that province. The total demand for each province is estimated from the total demand for Panama, which represents total disappearance, e.g., production plus imports. The total demand is prorated to the individual provinces on the basis of the relative total popu-

TABLE 4.5. ● PRODUCTION OF EDIBLE BEANS BY PROVINCE, 1960–70

Year	Bocas del Toro	Chiriqui	Veraguas	Herrera	Los Santos	Cocle	Panama	Colon	Darien	Country Total
1960-61	0.60	29.00	33.90	13.20	17.10	8.10	9.30	2.70	0.80	114.70
1961-62	0.20	56.30	52.10	12.20	9.70	5.80	11.40	1.50	0.10	149.30
1962-63	1.00	52.20	57.10	14.50	10.70	9.10	12.90	1.10	0.20	158.80
1963-64	0.10	39.50	30.90	6.10	13.50	6.30	7.80	1.50	0.10	105.80
1964-65	0.20	29.00	30.70	8.40	7.60	3.70	8.50	1.20	2.00	91.30
1965-66	0.05	33.40	66.20	9.80	15.30	14.90	9.00	3.50	0.10	152.25
1966-67	0.05	49.60	58.20	6.40	10.80	9.60	20.00	2.30	4.20	161.15
1967-68	0.05	27.80	65.00	7.80	6.70	5.90	10.50	2.00	4.30	130.05
1968-69	0.05	23.70	48.10	5.80	7.40	11.20	7.70	3.00	4.30	111.25
1969-70	0.05	31.00	38.60	6.50	7.20	7.30	11.90	2.40	4.30	109.25
Average	0.23	37.15	45.08	9.07	10.60	8.19	10.90	2.12	2.04	125.38
Percent	0.2	29.6	36.0	7.2	8.5	6.5	8.7	1.7	1.6	100.0

Source: Estadística Panameña: Información Agropecuaria.

TABLE 4.6. • SUPPLY AND UTILIZATION OF RICE, CORN, AND BEANS BY PROVINCE, 1969-70 (000 QUINTALS)

	Bocas del Toro	Chiriqui	Veraguas	Herrera	Los Santos	Cocle	Panama	Colon	Darien	Total without Imports	Imports	Total with Imports
Rice (Rough)												
Production	6.8	1,368.5	761.0	260.1	281.9	559.9	223.1	56.7	125.0	3,643.0		
Home Consumption	1.4	275.0	525.0	225.0	250.0	200.0	175.0	45.0	35.0	1,731.4		
Marketings	5.4	1,093.5	236.0	35.1	31.9	359.9	48.1	11.7	90.0	1,911.6		
Market Demand	102.8	328.3	0.0	0.0	0.0	101.3	1,058.5	298.2	22.5	1,911.6		
Surplus or Deficit	-97.4	765.2	236.0	35.1	31.9	258.6	-1,010.4	-286.5	67.5	0.0		
Corn (Shelled)												
Production	9.6	475.6	441.2	201.0	338.2	120.4	204.3	50.9	87.9	1,929.1		
Home Consumption	6.9	96.2	151.7	46.3	53.9	70.0	60.0	13.7	2.7	501.4		
Feed and Seed	0.7	172.4	134.6	88.8	239.4	38.6	90.0	21.7	1.7	787.9		
Marketings	2.0	207.0	154.9	65.9	44.9	11.8	54.3	15.5	83.5	639.8	50.0	689.8
Market Demand	25.7	92.8	0.0	11.7	3.6	24.4	422.5	93.8	15.3	689.8		689.8
Surplus or Deficit	-23.7	114.2	154.9	54.2	41.3	-12.6	-368.2	-78.3	68.2	-50.0	50.0	0.0
Edible Beans (Shelled)												
Production	0.05	31.0	38.6	6.5	7.2	7.3	11.9	2.4	4.3	109.25		
Home Consumption	0.01	11.0	16.5	5.5	5.4	4.0	9.3	1.9	1.0	54.61		
Marketings	0.04	20.0	22.1	1.0	1.8	3.3	2.6	0.5	3.3	54.64		54.64
Market Demand	3.04	6.8	0.0	0.0	0.0	4.9	30.9	8.3	0.7	54.64		54.64
Surplus or Deficit	-3.00	13.2	22.1	1.0	1.8	-1.6	-28.3	-7.8	2.6	0.00		

Source: Estadística Panameña: Información Agropecuaria.

lation (urban plus rural) as reported in the preliminary 1970 population census.

As evident in the upper portion of Table 4.6, 47.5% of rice produced during 1969–70 was used for home consumption. Utilization for seed is included in the volumes shown for home use. The fraction of total rice production consumed directly by the producer varies from 20% in Chiriqui to 88% in Los Santos. This fraction is relatively high in the provinces characterized by small producers such as Veraguas, Herrera, Los Santos, Panama, and Colon.

The market demand for rice is heavily concentrated in Panama and Colon provinces, making them major deficit areas. In addition to the marketings from their own area, these two provinces required nearly 1.3 million quintals of rough rice from other areas in 1969–70. The major surplus provinces supplying the rice to meet this deficit are Chiriqui, Veraguas, and Cocle. Bocas del Toro is a deficit area, and Herrera, Los Santos, and Darien market only limited volumes beyond the local market demand.

The supply and utilization of corn by province for 1969–70 are shown in the center section of Table 4.6. For the entire country, 501,400 quintals (26% of production) were used for food by the producer and his family, and 787,900 quintals (41% of production) were used by the farmer for poultry and livestock feed and for seed. The percentage used for home consumption is quite high in Bocas del Toro (72%) and Cocle (58%) but quite low in Darien (3%). The percentage used for feed and seed is high in Los Santos (71%) and low in Darien (2%) and Bocas del Toro (7%).

Of the 639,800 quintals of corn reaching the market in 1969–70, 207,000 quintals (32%) came from Chiriqui, 154,900 quintals (24%) from Veraguas, and 83,500 quintals (13%) from Darien. These three provinces plus Herrera and Los Santos represented the corn surplus areas. Four provinces (Bocas del Toro, Cocle, Panama, and Colon) were deficit areas, with 76% of the total corn deficit concentrated in Panama. A total of 50,000 quintals of corn were imported to balance the deficit of corn production during the period. Most of the imports were used by the poultry and livestock feed industry in the vicinity of Panama City.

Patterns of utilization of edible beans during 1969–70 are similar to those for corn (Table 4.6). Chiriqui and Veraguas are the major surplus provinces, while Panama and Colon are the major deficit provinces. Fifty percent of the beans are used for home consumption, so that only 54,640 quintals moved through market channels. Of this volume, over 56.5% (30,900 quintals) was consumed in Panama province and another 15% (8,300 quintals) was consumed in Colon.

Supply and Demand Projections for Grains

Rapid strides have been made during the sixties in increasing yields and production of rice and corn. Yet, the need exists for expanding output at an increasing rate during the seventies. Domestic demand for rough rice is growing at the rate of nearly 5,400 metric tons annually and demand for corn at the rate of about 700 tons annually, excluding the increasing demand for corn used in animal feeds.

On the basis of past trends in production and consumption, Panama will have a small surplus in rice production in 1975 and 1980 (Table 4.7). The demand projections developed by the Sector Study Commission (SSC), however, suggest that future demand for rice is likely to exceed past demand. The SSC projected the 1980 apparent consumption of rough rice to be 250,000 metric tons, compared to the trend projection of 213,500 tons. The trend projection for rice should be interpreted as a low projection. If actual demand in 1980 is as little as 3% above the trend, Panama will have a rice deficit unless production can be increased more rapidly than it was during the 1960s.

Excluding the potential increases in demand for corn in livestock and poultry feeds, the trend projections of the supply and demand for corn in 1975 and 1980 indicate that Panama will be self-sufficient in corn production during most of the 1970s (Table 4.7). Corn is being imported for poultry feeds, and increased imports will be needed if the poultry industry is to continue to grow at past rates. Sorghum can be substituted on nearly a one-to-one basis for corn in poultry feeds. The government's price support program for sorghum has encouraged some rice producers to plant sorghum as a second crop. The initial results of this program are encouraging. It seems likely that within the next five years, producers will develop enough knowledge of different varieties, proper timing, and disease control to produce sorghum successfully. If so, the annual combined production of corn and sorghum could be nearly 160,000 metric tons by 1980, nearly twice the 1966–70 average annual production of corn alone. If this were the case, there would be no need to import corn for poultry feeds by the late 1970s.

The possibility of eliminating the projected deficit in bean production seems remote. The projections of imports in 1975 range from 3,400 to 5,800 metric tons, while those for 1980 range from 5,000 to 6,800 tons (Table 4.7). Prices of edible beans are likely to increase, but this is not expected to have a significant impact on production.[2]

Wheat imports are expected to increase to 55,800 metric tons in 1975 and to 67,800 tons in 1980. The possibilities for substituting fish

---

2. Further information on the possibilities of increasing bean production can be found in Phillips, 1971.

TABLE 4.7. • PROJECTED SUPPLY AND DEMAND BALANCES FOR GRAINS, 1975 AND 1980

Item	Production 1975 (000 MT)	1980	Apparent Consumption 1975 (000 MT)	1980	Surplus (Deficit) 1975 (000 MT)	1980
Rice (Rough)						
a. Trend	189.5	218.3	186.6	213.5	2.9	4.8
b. Potential[a]	207.1	213.8	205.0	250.0	2.9	(38.2)
Corn and Sorghum						
a. Trend[b]	86.0	91.0	86.0	89.5	--	1.5
b. Potential[a]	106.9	159.2	122.6	159.2	(15.7)	--
Beans						
a. Trend	3.9	3.0	9.7	9.8	(5.8)	(6.8)
b. Potential[a]	5.7	5.8	9.1	10.8	(3.4)	(5.0)
Wheat[c]	--	--	55.8	67.8	(55.8)	(67.8)
Flour[d]	--	--	0.7	0.7	(0.7)	(0.7)

[a]Potential projections are based on Phillips, 1971. The projections of potential corn production in 1980 include 85,700 tons of sorghum. The projections of potential corn consumption include estimates of the amount of corn and sorghum required for livestock and poultry feeds.

[b]The trend projections of corn consumption do not allow for additional corn or sorghum needed to supply an enlarged livestock and poultry production.

[c]Based on the 1966-70 trend.

[d]Based on the 1966-70 average imports.

or potato flour for wheat flour are limited by technical considerations. The costs of restricting imports or attempting to promote domestic production of wheat are likely to exceed the benefits.

LIVESTOCK, POULTRY, AND FISH

Except for hogs, the production of livestock products has increased substantially since 1960. Beef production increased by nearly 80% during the 1960s, from 19,200 metric tons in 1960 to 34,400 tons in 1970. Poultry production increased by 66% during the same period, from 4,100 to 6,800 tons. Egg production increased by nearly 50%, production of fresh milk by 63%.

The 1960–70 period was also a period of rapid growth of the fishing industry. However, the output growth rates for fishery products varied considerably from product to product. In general terms, production of fresh fish increased by 380%, from 11,400 to 54,900 metric tons. Fresh fish production reached as high as 80,000 tons in 1968. Production of shellfish, on the other hand, increased by only 25%, from 5,500 to 6,900 tons during the 1960–70 period.

At producer prices, the value of output of the livestock sector is approximately four times that of the fishing industry. Nevertheless, fishing is an important source of foreign exchange earnings. Shrimp exports in 1970 were valued at B/10,168,000. Exports of fresh and frozen beef, on the other hand, were only B/2,189,000. The fishing industry is expected to become increasingly important during the 1970s.

Beef and Milk Production

According to the agricultural census of 1971, Panama had nearly 1.24 million head of cattle. The national herd grew at the compounded annual rate of 4.9% during the 1961–71 period. Sample surveys in the intervening years indicate above average growth until 1968 and an average of 3.7% between 1969 and 1971.[3] The provinces of Chiriqui, Veraguas, and Los Santos accounted for two-thirds of the cattle population in 1971. Smaller concentrations of cattle are found in Herrera, Cocle, and parts of Panama provinces. The Atlantic slope and the province of Darien are practically devoid of cattle because of the lack of access roads.

It is estimated that out of a total of approximately 100,000 farms some 28,000 had cattle in 1966. Nearly 22,000 farms had fewer than 20 head, while the 570 largest farms with 200 head or more each accounted for about 55% of the cattle. On the average, approximately 60% of the available agricultural credit goes to livestock producers. Assuming that the livestock credit is distributed evenly on the basis of heads of cattle, over 30% of total agricultural credit goes to less than 1% of Panama's farmers. Cattle raising is a secondary enterprise on about three-fourths of the farms having cattle. Beef and milk production are joint enterprises on many farms. It is estimated that 6% to 8% of the total cattle are kept for milking.

Out of 71 million liters of milk produced in 1970, 27.6 million (39%) were purchased for the production of condensed, evaporated, and dry milk. About 17 million liters (24%) were used for pasteurized milk,

---

3. Haim Harel, Estudio Sobre La Economía de La Producción Ganadera en Panamá, 1971, November 1972.

and most of the remainder was consumed on farms where produced. Nearly 10,000 metric tons of ice cream were produced in 1969, partly from condensed milk and the other dairy products included in the 27.6 million liters mentioned above.[4]

Milk production has been relatively constant since 1966. Total milk supply is not adequate to meet total demand at prevailing prices. Milk products imported include milk solids, nonfat dry milk, butter, butter oil, evaporated milk, and cheese. Some of these items are used for the manufacture of ice cream. Imported dry milk is being reconstituted for sale in the Canal Zone but is not sold elsewhere in Panama. No fresh milk is imported.

Considering past trends, milk production is projected to be 96,300 metric tons in 1975 and 112,900 tons by 1980 (Table 4.8). The trend projections of demand for fresh milk are identical to those of production. The SSC demand projections shown in Table 4.8 take into account the income elasticity for milk, estimated to be 0.72. The SSC projected total milk consumption to be 113,400 tons in 1975 and 144,800 tons by 1980. Using the trend estimates of production and the SSC estimates of demand, imports of milk products on a fresh milk basis would be nearly 32,000 tons by 1980.

The trend projections of milk production appear to be rather optimistic. There was no evidence in the early 1970s that the large dairy farmers were planning either to increase or improve their herds substantially, nor were any large-scale herd improvement programs under way for smaller producers. Furthermore, given the existing cost and price structure, there seems to be little incentive for the average producer to increase his investment in dairying. Although the SSC demand projections appear to be somewhat high, they nevertheless suggest that increased imports of dairy products and continued upward pressure on the price of domestically produced milk are likely throughout the decade.

Beef production increased from 19,200 metric tons in 1960 to 34,400 tons in 1970. This increase is equivalent to a compounded annual rate of approximately 5.4%; beef exports increased from 1,100 to 3,500 tons during the same period. Domestic beef prices remained relatively stable during most of the 1960s, while export prices increased in the late 1960s and early 1970s. The more favorable export prices encouraged increased exports and resulted in upward pressures on domestic prices.

Based on past trends, beef production is projected to reach 42,100 metric tons in 1975 and 49,500 tons by 1980. Demand for beef is projected at 38,800 tons in 1975 and 44,000 tons in 1980. Therefore, projected beef exports would be 5,500 tons by the end of the decade; however, these projections would appear somewhat optimistic. Panama has the potential to produce far more beef than it currently does, but that

---

4. Louis F. Herrmann, Beef and Milk Production and Marketing in Panama, American Technical Assistance Corporation, December 1971.

TABLE 4.8. ● **PROJECTED SUPPLY AND DEMAND BALANCES FOR LIVESTOCK PRODUCTS AND FISH, 1975 AND 1980**

Item		Production 1975 (000 MT)	1980	Apparent Consumption 1975 (000 MT)	1980	Surplus (Deficit) 1975 (000 MT)	1980
Beef							
a.	Trend[a]	41.9	49.2	37.5	43.7	4.3	5.5
b.	SSC[b]	42.1	49.5	38.8	44.0	4.3	5.5
Pork							
a.	Trend	3.7	3.9	3.7	3.9	--	--
b.	SSC[b]	3.6	3.8	5.3	7.0	(1.7)	(3.2)
Poultry							
a.	Trend	7.5	8.8	7.5	8.8	--	--
b.	SSC[b]	7.0	8.8	10.9	15.3	(3.9)	(7.2)
Canned Meat							
a.	Trend	2.7	3.7	6.1	7.8	(3.4)	(4.1)
b.	SSC[b]	1.1	1.1	5.3	6.9	(4.2)	(5.8)
Fresh Milk							
a.	Trend	96.3	112.9	96.3	112.9	--	--
b.	SSC[b]	101.1	120.0	113.4	144.8	(12.3)	(24.8)
Eggs							
a.	Trend	7.0	7.6	7.1	8.0	(0.1)	(0.4)
b.	SSC[b]	7.8	8.7	9.0	11.3	(1.2)	(2.6)
Fresh Fish		104.1	135.1	104.1	135.1	--	--
Shellfish		6.9	7.4	1.6	1.8	5.3	5.6

[a]The linear trend projections in this chapter are based on data from the Dirección de Estadística y Censo.

[b]The projections are presented in: Randall A. Hoffmann, Agricultural Sector Analysis and Planning, Panama, end of tour report, USAID, April 1971.

potential cannot be realized without substantial long-run investments, both by the government and by private producers.

The productivity of land devoted to cattle production has changed very little during the sixties. The stocking rate, on the average, is about 1.1 animal units per hectare. As cattle numbers have increased, an approximately equal number of additional hectares of land have been brought into use. In view of the large amount of land still uncultivated, this type of development can be expected to continue. The extension of the Pan-American Highway into Darien, for example, will open a large area of land well suited to livestock. Future road construction into the northern provinces of Bocas del Toro, Veraguas, and parts of Colon will make available still further acreages of relatively cheap, undeveloped lands for which the best use, at least in the short run, is probably livestock. Even in the comparatively well-developed provinces of Chiriqui, Veraguas, Cocle, and Los Santos, significant areas of land remain unexploited. Thus the availability of pastureland does not appear to be a limiting factor in livestock production.[5]

Because of the extensive nature of livestock production and the generally low rate of return derived from such activity, it might be expected that competition for pastureland would develop in some areas. This competition appears to be occurring to a limited extent in Veraguas, Cocle, and parts of Los Santos. In these areas, flatlands suitable for mechanized agriculture are increasingly in demand for the production of crops, principally sugarcane and rice. Good land in these areas is valued at B/200 per hectare and above. If land values continue to increase, alternative land uses will cause further declines in cattle production unless new production technology is introduced.

Government policies have had a discernible impact on the livestock industry, especially since the late sixties. Meat prices are regulated at the retail level in the Panama City and Colon areas. In theory, the price of all beef, except certain choice cuts, is controlled. Retail price levels have not been changed, even though the average price of cattle on the hoof has risen from B/0.17 to B/0.21 per pound. In practice, price controls have not been very effective, and the actual economic loss to cattlemen from price controls probably has not been excessive.

Meat exports are regulated by Executive Decree No. 2, January 4, 1971, which states that meat exports shall be prohibited between March 15 and August 1 of each year until such time as conditions permit exports throughout the year. In practice, these dates are not always adhered to, with the consequence that the rancher is not able to efficiently schedule animals for export. Export quotas for meat are established monthly, are based on estimates of the number of cattle available for

5. J. P. Rourke, A Review and Appraisal of Factors Affecting Livestock Production in Panama, GOP report, February 1973.

slaughter, and are not to exceed one animal for each ten slaughtered for domestic consumption.

The Agrarian Reform Program is based on Law No. 37, September 1962. It was viewed primarily as an instrument for effecting change in the traditional system of land tenure through voluntary or compulsory dissolution of large estates and the settlement of large numbers of landless campesinos on plots of their own. As far as the livestock industry is concerned, agrarian reform would not appear at first glance to pose much of a threat. Article 12 provides that lands not fulfilling their social obligation may be expropriated. However, compliance requires only that at least two-thirds of the total property be cultivated and that pastures carry at least one animal for each 2 hectares. Article 37 further strengthens the position of cattlemen by stating that properties fulfilling their social function may not be expropriated, regardless of size. Nevertheless, Article 41 provides that if an existing ranch is deemed to constitute an obstacle of either a technical or economic nature to the establishment of an asentamiento, the ranch may be expropriated even if it is admittedly fulfilling its social obligation or falls within a category that supposedly is not subject to expropriation. The government's efforts to expand the asentamiento program beginning in 1969 have increased cattlemen's awareness of Article 41.[6]

The Ministry of Agriculture has established a five-year program (1972–76) for livestock with the following objectives: (1) providing additional production for increased domestic demand and an increase in export earnings, (2) increasing the net rate of return of the livestock industry through improved efficiency in the utilization of its natural and financial resources, (3) ensuring that the profits accruing to the livestock sector are divided more equitably by providing special assistance to small producers, and (4) promoting and strengthening the programs affecting animal health and sanitation. The five-year program emphasizes the improvement of livestock management in general and particularly seeks to encourage rotational grazing of pastures, improve the control of disease and parasites, promote routine use of salt and minerals, and start crossbreeding programs with European breeds. To achieve the government's goal of a rate of sustained growth of the livestock industry sufficient to provide for growing domestic consumption and increased exports will require significant progress in all phases of the industry, i.e., breeding, feeding, and management.

Considerable progress has been made in upgrading the quality of cattle. The vast majority of the beef cattle show evidence of Cebu breeding, and a surprisingly large number are of predominantly Brahman blood. In the specialized dairy sector, one finds numerous herds of pure-

---

6. Beginning in 1969, the Agrarian Reform Commission initiated a program to acquire lands and organize cooperative farms called asentamientos.

bred or high-grade Holstein-Friesian or Brown Swiss. The process of upgrading herds could be accelerated through greater use of artificial insemination in both beef and dairy herds.

Most serious deficiencies in livestock production technology are found in management and nutrition. The greatest potential for increased meat production lies in pasture improvement. In 1970, about 15% of the 1,112,000 hectares in pasture were in natural grasses and 85% in artificially planted grasses.[7] Of the planted pastures, perhaps as much as 90% is planted in Faragua. While Faragua is a relatively good grass, it requires good management to ensure that it is grazed at the nutritious point. Some of the more progressive ranchers are beginning to experiment with improved grasses such as Pangola digitgrass and African Star grass. These offer higher yields, greater palatability, and faster recovery after grazing and are more responsive to fertilization. Properly managed, they have a much higher protein content.[8]

A few progressive ranchers are beginning to use fertilizer on pasture. Sales of fertilizer for this use increased from about 500 short tons in 1968 to 1,800 tons in 1972. Based on the recommended minimum application of 1,200 lb/ha/yr, one may conclude that even in 1972 only 3,000 hectares (less than 1% of the total pastureland) were fertilized.

Cattlemen generally make little or no effort to mitigate the effects of the prolonged dry season through the use of irrigation or by making hay. The effect of the dry season is reflected in the marked seasonality of marketing and in the sharp drop in weight of cattle slaughtered during the dry season. Data from the national abbatoir in Panama reveal that slaughter cattle weigh from 840 to 925 pounds liveweight during the rainy season and from 760 to 840 pounds per head during the dry season. This weight differential is a serious loss of meat production that could be partly overcome by improved range management.

Perhaps the most serious problem associated with poor nutrition and poor management is the low calving percentage, estimated to be between 40% and 50%.[9] Because of this low rate, genetic improvement is seriously handicapped since virtually all females must be retained as replacements and little selection is possible. If the calving percentage could be increased to, say, 60%, fears that excessive slaughter of cows would retard growth of the national herd could be overcome, and ranchers would benefit from culling of undesirable cows.[10]

7. Dirección de Estadística y Censo, Existencia de Ganado Vacuno en La República: Años 1961 a 1972, Panama, November 1972.

8. A complete report of the MAG/FAO pasture improvement program is found in Oscar Miranda, Mejora de Pastos y Cultivos Forrajeros, Panamá, Producción del Ganado de Carne, United Nations, Panama, 1973.

9. Jaime Aizpurua, Problemas, Situación Actual y Posibles Soluciones de La Actividad Ganadera en Panamá, December 1971.

10. For additional information on the impact of increased rates of female slaughter on cattle inventory projections see Louis Herrmann, An Analysis of Livestock Production Prospects in Panama, GOP report, February 1973.

Although Panama is fortunate in not having any serious livestock diseases, failure to adequately control internal and external parasites contributes to loss of condition and increased mortality, particularly of young animals. It is hoped that the ministry's program to increase cattle production will make cattlemen more aware of the economic benefits of parasite control.

It is suggested frequently that the livestock industry is not sufficiently remunerative to encourage further investment in improved pastures or cattle. This thesis is probably accurate if the value of land is included in the cost of production calculations and existing technology is assumed. Rising prices undoubtedly would make beef and milk production more profitable, but it is not clear that higher prices would hasten introduction of improved technology.

Although producers may consider the prices of beef and milk to be "low" relative to their production costs, prices appear reasonable by international standards. Beef prices at B/0.20 to B/0.22 per pound live-weight are higher than in any country in Central America except possibly Costa Rica. Milk prices at B/0.15 to B/0.19 per liter of milk for pasteurization and B/0.09 to B/0.11 per liter for industrial milk are high by international standards.

Price increases can serve to signal increased government interest in promoting cattle production and may encourage cattlemen to increase the size of their herds. In the long run, however, Panama must concentrate on increasing the efficiency of cattle production, lowering production costs, and increasing the amount of milk and beef produced per hectare. Achievement of these objectives will require sustained cooperation of the government and private sectors in an effort to improve the management, feeding, and quality of the beef and milk herds.

Hogs

Patterns of pork production have changed very little since 1960.

The SSC projected pork production to be 3,600 metric tons in 1975 and 3,800 tons by 1980. Total consumption was projected at 5,300 tons for 1975 and 7,000 tons in 1980 (Table 4.8).

The relatively high cost of feed grains is the main factor limiting growth in pork production. At present price levels, even efficient operators cannot produce a pound of pork as cheaply as cattlemen can produce a pound of beef. As a result, grain-fed pork is not price-competitive with beef except when prepared as specialty items. Furthermore, it generally is cheaper to import specialty pork items than to produce them domestically.

Several approaches could be taken to encourage increased pork production. The government could restrict imports of pork items and allow domestic pork prices to increase. Higher prices and the availability of close substitutes would limit the amount of pork demanded and in turn the rate of increase in production. An alternative method would be to import feed grains under long-term loans whenever possible. This approach would lower feed prices and increase production in the short run but would have little long-run impact on production unless supplemented with other programs. A third approach would be to concentrate first on increasing domestic production of feed grains and then introducing improved hog production techniques as real grain prices decline. This last alternative seems best suited to Panama's present situation.

Poultry

The production of poultry meat increased at an average annual rate of approximately 6% during the 1960s.[11] Total production in 1970 was 6,800 metric tons compared to 4,100 tons in 1960. The largest increases in production occurred after 1965.

Large, commercial producers supply about 50% of total poultry meat production. The market share of large producers increased steadily during 1960–70, and further increases are expected. The three largest commercial operations are completely integrated. They hatch baby chicks, manufacture feed, raise and process their own broilers, and market their produce to the last point-of-sale customers.

Modern technology for commercial poultry production is used; the commercial production of both broilers and eggs is technically advanced and efficient. The seven major feed manufacturers produce a wide range of feeds, including superconcentrates for broilers and layers. Vaccines and medicines are readily available through the larger producers and several chemical companies.

Estimates of the cost of production of broilers range from B/0.34 per pound for small producers to B/0.28 per pound for large, commercial producers with feed costs typically accounting for 50% to 60% of total production costs. The high production costs reported by large, commercial producers are due partly to accelerated depreciation rates and high administrative costs. Reductions in feed costs and profit rates offer the greatest possibilities for lowering total production costs. It seems unlikely that such reductions will occur rapidly enough to substantially lower the market price of poultry meat in the seventies.

Projecting past trends, the supply of poultry meat would continue to equal demand (Table 4.8). If the high income elasticity of poultry meat and the expected increases in income are taken into account,

11. This section draws heavily on Mora y Medina, La Avicultura en La República de Panamá, Ministry of Agriculture and Livestock, 1971; Charles P. Swett, Poultry Production and Marketing, Sector Study Commission, December 1971.

production is projected to be 3,900 metric tons short of demand in 1975 and 7,200 tons short by 1980. This shortage suggests a continued upward pressure on poultry prices even if production costs are reduced.

The production of eggs is projected to continue to be less than demand. It is estimated that by 1980 egg imports will account for 5% to 20% of total consumption, depending on the vigor of the government's efforts to maintain stable egg prices. The coefficient of income elasticity for eggs has been estimated to be 1.8, which is considerably higher than the income elasticity for other major food items.[12]

Fish

Commercial fishing accounts for about 2% of Panama's gross domestic product (GDP) but represents the third most important food export by value. Shrimp are the most important product of the fishing industry. Exports in 1972 were valued at B/14,584,000, compared to B/11,953,000 in 1971.[13] The increased value was entirely due to rising market prices. In terms of weight, the total shrimp catch has remained relatively constant during 1960–70. It is believed that production of white shrimp may have reached its limit consistent with conservation measures. However, since further price increases for shrimp are expected, the value of shrimp exports may continue to increase.

There are two fish meal plants in Panama. Exports of fish meal and fish oil increased during 1972, both in weight and value. Fish meal exports in 1972 were valued at B/1,432,000, compared to B/982,000 in 1971. Fish oil exports in 1972 were valued at B/270,000. The total value of fish meal and fish oil exports increased from B/330,000 in 1969 to B/1,702,000 in 1972.

The large-scale commercial processing of scallops is a new development in the Panamanian fishing industry. Three processing companies exported about B/2 million of scallops to the United States in 1972. The outlook for this new export industry is promising, both in terms of exchange earnings and increased employment.

Panama has only one sardine processing plant, which cans large sardines in tomato sauce for the domestic market. This plant has been assisted by the government through import controls on sardines.

Most of the food fish for domestic consumption are caught by artisan fishermen. The government of Panama and the Food and Agriculture Organization of the United Nations (FAO) have encouraged the formation of cooperatives by small fishermen in an effort to improve the com-

12. Randall A. Hoffmann, Agricultural Sector Analysis and Planning, Panama, end of tour report, USAID, April 1971.
13. American Embassy, Industrial Outlook Report: Fishing Industry, Panama, December 1972.

mercialization of their product and to increase the credit available to fishermen wishing to expand their operations. The Inter-American Development Bank (IDB) also has shown interest in the possibilities for promoting artisan fishing.

Future growth in the fishing industry will require diversification. The FAO is assisting the Panamanian government in an exploratory fishing project to determine the potential of deepwater fishing.[14] Its research has verified the abundance of deepwater, medium-sized, red shrimp in the Pacific. Efforts are also being made to improve the marketing of fish and to increase the utilization of larger fish usually discarded by shrimp trawlers. The FAO also is assisting in development of shark fishing, and processed shark has proven to be an acceptable substitute for imported cod in the Panamanian market. Artisan fishermen have been reluctant to fish for shark, however, due to the risks involved when using small boats.

The Ministry of Commerce and Industry is promoting an aquaculture project to stimulate production and consumption of fish in agrarian settlements and communities. This program is receiving technical assistance from experts of AID and Auburn University. The project consists of raising fingerlings in hatchery ponds at the National Institute of Agriculture at Divisa and distributing them to the agrarian settlements.

Panama's fishing fleet consists of 238 shrimp boats and some 20 purse seiners; the number and size of shrimp boats are fixed by decree. Shrimp fishing frequently is prohibited during the February-April period to protect young, white shrimp during their most rapid growth stage. Two major limitations on the expansion of the fishing industry are lack of a fishing port and obsolescence of the shrimp fleet. Government investments in these areas could have a major impact by reducing the industry's costs even if no major gains in production were achieved.

In August 1971, the World Bank made a $3.4 million loan to the National Bank of Panama for the partial financing of a $5.4 million project to renovate the shrimp fleet without increasing the total number of boats by financing 40 new shrimp trawlers to replace existing wooden boats. This project has not progressed as rapidly as anticipated, however, because shrimp boat operators appear reluctant to absorb the losses from retiring their old boats, which have no resale value or use in other types of fishing.

Panama is attempting to encourage its shipbuilding industry. Boats constructed outside the country are subject to a 15% import tax, and a new regulation issued in July 1972 states that only boats constructed in Panamanian shipyards can fish for shrimp in Panamanian waters, with the exception of boats to be acquired under the World Bank loan.

14. United Nations Food and Agriculture Organization, Proyecto Regional de Desarrollo Pesquero en Centro América. Rome, September 1972.

There is only one public shipyard, and it offers both steel-hull and wood-hull capability. International Protein, Inc., and Modern Fiberglass Company have established a private shipyard for the construction of fiberglass shrimp boats. There are several other small private yards. Both public and private shipyards appear to be prospering with the growth of the fishing industry.

Although no new port facilities will be in operation prior to the late 1970s, the 1970s should be prosperous years for the fishing industry.[15] Given the age and condition of the fishing fleet, the availability of funds for modern shrimp boats, and the laws encouraging domestic shipbuilding, the shipyards should prosper at least until the late 1970s. The weight of shrimp and fish meal exports should increase once larger boats are available for fishing deeper water. Meanwhile, it appears that further price increases for seafoods are likely. New port facilities, once available, will help the industry lower its marketing costs. Improved marketing facilities should result in a better product at the retail level and encourage increased domestic consumption of fish.

FRUITS AND VEGETABLES

Fruits and vegetables play a major role in the agricultural economy.

Vegetables and plantains account for 8% to 9% of the value of food consumed in the country, and bananas account for over half the nation's total exports.

Potatoes and other root crops, tomatoes, lettuce, cabbage, carrots, onions, beets, and green peppers are Panama's most important vegetable crops. Plantains are included in the "vegetable" category because they are used as a vegetable or "potato alternative" by many consumers. When so included, plantains account for nearly one-third of consumer expenditures on vegetables. The wholesale value of tomatoes in 1972 was B/822,000, or approximately 6% of the total value of the major vegetables. Only 10% of total tomato production reaches the fresh market; the rest are industrial tomatoes used for canning, juice, paste, and catsup. The 1972 wholesale values of the other major horticultural crops are shown in Table 4.9. Potatoes and other root crops accounted for nearly 45% of the total wholesale value during the 1972 season.

Panama's vegetable production is centered primarily in the provinces of Chiriqui, Herrera, Los Santos, and Cocle. Tomatoes, onions, and peppers are grown in all four provinces; but nearly all the nation's potatoes, lettuce, cabbage, carrots, and beets are produced in Chiriqui province.

The production data for vegetables suggest that substantial year-to-year changes exist in the area planted and in the yields of most of the

---

15. Livesey, Henderson, and partners, Estudio Puerto Pesquero, Ministerio de Comercio e Industrias, Panama, 1972.

TABLE 4.9. ● ESTIMATED WHOLESALE VALUE OF HORTICULTURAL CROPS, 1972

Item	Value (000 balboas)	Total Values (000 balboas)
Tomatoes	822	
Head Lettuce	675	
Cabbage	575	
Carrots	461	
Onions	306	
Beets	175	
Green Peppers	125	
Subtotal (Vegetables)		3,139
Potatoes	1,841	
Yuca	1,610	
Name	1,542	
Otoe	967	
Subtotal (Root Crops)		5,960
Plantain	4,438	4,438
Grand Total		B/13,537

Source: John Malcolm, Vegetables in Panama's Development Program, An Assessment and Recommendations, USAID, February 1973.

major crops. These wide fluctuations have been attributed to many causes. Among the most important factors are poor weather, lack of seed at planting time, low prices the previous year, and labor shortages at critical periods such as transplanting time. The reported retail prices for vegetables show much less variation than production.

Production of most vegetables is highly seasonal. Crops are planted at the end of the rainy season and grown through the dry (summer) season when diseases and insects can be controlled most easily. Only yuca and carrots have true "off-season" production peaks. Efforts are being made to equalize the supply of some products over the year.

Specialists at the University of Panama have encouraged the grafting of tomato plants onto wild rootstock to allow the production of "winter" tomatoes. Some producers are trying to grow off-season vegetables using new pesticides, herbicides, and disease-resistant plant varieties. Efforts are being made to encourage the storage of potatoes and onions. It is expected that increased quantities of vegetables will be processed in the future, either canned, frozen, or dried.

Vegetable production costs are relatively high. The cost estimates developed by Chen of the Institute of Economic Development are shown in Table 4.10. Chen's estimates of yields per hectare probably are fairly optimistic, especially in the case of green peppers. Nevertheless, his calculations suggest that vegetable production generally should be reasonably profitable for efficient producers.[16]

Most vegetable producers appear to minimize their risks by planting only small amounts. For most crops, the average planting is below one hectare. Average plantings of industrial tomatoes are not much larger; it is estimated that in 1972, 450 farmers planted 600 hectares. Their risks were reduced further through contracts with canners, but returns were reduced also.

New roads in Chiriqui province are expected to open areas for vegetable production during the seventies. It seems unlikely, however, that new roads in the provinces of Bocas del Toro and Darien will be significant factors in increased vegetable production. The high rainfall in the Bocas del Toro region would make vegetable growing a marginal operation. Vegetable production in the Darien region, even at the higher altitudes, is likely to be delayed due to the nearly complete absence of commercial producers in that area.

The production of potatoes, tomatoes, and onions is encouraged by import limitations and price controls. The Junta Nacional de Mercado de Papas has had reasonable success in maintaining the wholesale price of potatoes in recent years. The price was maintained at B/7.00 per quintal throughout 1972 by limiting the amount of potatoes marketed.[17]

Projections of the supply and demand for vegetables must be interpreted with care. The basic data upon which the projections are based are very weak. The linear trend projections based on 1960–70 data suggest that Panama will be self-sufficient in the production of most vegetables, except possibly potatoes and onions (Table 4.11). The SSC projected the demand for vegetables to increase at a somewhat faster rate during the 1970s than in the 1960s. As a result, the SSC projec-

16. Additional information on the cost of production of potatoes and onions can be found in Cándida Fuéntes, Observaciones sobre Costos de Producción y Problemas Técnicos del Cultivo de Algunas Hortalizas, GOP report, Panama, December 1972.
17. John Malcolm, Vegetables in Panama's Development Program—An Assessment and Recommendations, GOP report, Panama, February, 1973.

TABLE 4.10. ● PRODUCTION COSTS FOR SELECTED CROPS AND ESTIMATED RETURNS

Cost and Returns	Potato	Tomato Processing	Tomato Fresh Market	Onions	Peppers	Cabbage	Lettuce	Carrots	Beets
Production Cost B/./ha	997.56	1,167.25	1,871.50	1,626.40	1,318.49	932.49	742.95	599.03	645.04
Yield q/ha	300	400	300	350	400	600	300	300	300
Cost B/./q	3.33	2.92	6.24	4.65	3.30	1.55	2.48	2.00	2.15
Estimated Value B/./q	7.00	3.00	15.00	9.00	16.00	6.00	13.00	10.00	11.00
Gross Return B/./ha	2,100.00	1,200.00	4,500.00	3,150.00	6,400.00	3,600.00	3,900.00	3,000.00	3,300.00
Net Return B/./ha	1,102.44	32.75	2,628.50	1,523.60	5,081.51	2,667.51	3,157.05	2,400.97	2,654.96

Source: A. M. Chen, Costos de Producción de Hortalizas en las Tierras Altas de Chiriquí y en las Provincias Centrales, Instituto de Fomento Económico, October 1971.

MAG Dirección General de Mercadeo, Precios Pagados por Mayoristas a los Agricultores y Traficantes en la Ciudad de Panamá por Mes: Años 1967-1971, February 1972.

Item	Production 1975 (000 MT)	Production 1980 (000 MT)	Apparent Consumption 1975 (000 MT)	Apparent Consumption 1980 (000 MT)	Surplus (Deficit) 1975 (000 MT)	Surplus (Deficit) 1980 (000 MT)
Bananas						
a. High[a]	1268	1525	508	577	760	948
b. Medium[b]	1188	1352	508	577	680	775
c. Low[c]	1130	1227	508	577	622	650
Oranges						
a. Trend	66.7	73.7	66.7	73.7	--	--
b. 1970 Output[d]	83.5	83.5	83.5	83.5	--	--
Pineapples						
a. Trend	6.3	7.1	6.3	7.1	--	--
b. SSC[e]	8.4	10.1	10.4	13.3	(2.0)	(3.2)
Coconuts						
a. Trend	22.4	17.4	6.0	--	16.4	17.4
Potatoes						
a. Trend	7.9	8.3	8.1	8.5	(0.2)	(0.2)
b. SSC	10.0	11.2	12.5	14.9	(2.5)	(3.7)
Other Root Crops						
a. Trend	61.8	73.3	61.8	73.3	--	--
b. SSC	54.7	63.8	58.0	70.9	(3.3)	(7.1)
Tomatoes						
a. Trend	34.2	41.2	34.2	41.2	--	--
b. SSC	34.5	41.4	43.2	47.4	(8.7)	(6.0)
Onions						
a. Trend	6.0	7.7	7.2	8.3	(1.2)	(0.6)
b. SSC	6.0	8.0	8.7	10.6	(2.7)	(2.6)
Lettuce and Cabbage						
a. Trend	9.7	11.4	9.7	11.4	--	--
b. SSC	11.0	13.3	11.6	14.6	(0.6)	(1.3)

[a]High projected exports for bananas based on 1960-70 trend.

[b]Medium projected exports for bananas based on FAO projections.

[c]Low projected exports for bananas based on the assumption that Panama would supply 10% of world market using USDA equilibrium projections.

[d]Orange production increased substantially in 1970 as new groves came into production. Some production problems exist, and total production may level off for several years. In 1973, the trend projections appeared to be very low estimates.

[e]Projections are in Hoffmann, 1971.

111

tions indicate a deficit in the production of most of the major vegetables (Table 4.11), but neither of these sets of projections takes into account possible price adjustments. It seems likely that Panama will continue to import seed potatoes and may find it necessary at times to import some types of onions. It is also likely that the prices of tomatoes, lettuce, and cabbage will adjust to equate domestic supply and demand without imports.

The SSC did not carry out any detailed studies of the fruit industry. The limited information available is summarized in the supply and demand projections shown in Table 4.11. Oranges appear to be in excess supply. Both the supply of and demand for pineapples are projected to increase; some producers are experimenting with new pineapple varieties and production techniques that will allow year-round harvesting. The supply and demand for coconuts are expected to decline.

Many specialists believe that Panama has the potential to export fruits and vegetables to the United States.[18] Among the items suggested as having export potential are tomatoes, green peppers, cantaloupes, watermelons, okra, yuca, avocados, artichokes, and asparagus. Some okra and peeled, frozen yuca have been exported on an irregular basis in the past. Items considered to have little or no export potential are pineapples, string beans, cabbage, broccoli, brussels sprouts, and cauliflower.[19]

Only top-quality produce is worth exporting. Such produce requires care in the selection of varieties; proper fertilization, pest control, and cultivation practices; and appropriate harvesting and packing procedures. The technical skill, experience, and marketing facilities required to deliver top-quality produce are still in short supply.

Potential exporters would require strong financial backing during the first two or three years of operation. Exports of fresh fruits and vegetables to the United States are likely to meet strong competition from Mexico and other Central American countries. Mexico has consistently increased its share of the winter and early spring market for most fresh vegetables in the United States. During the 1969–70 season, Mexico supplied 83% of cucumber imports, 99% of eggplant imports, 91% of pepper imports, 93% of tomato imports, and nearly 95% of strawberry imports.

Since the 1960s, numerous countries have attempted to sell fresh vegetables in the U.S. markets. Most have failed to attain or maintain a large volume of sales. Only Mexico, Canada, and the Bahamas have succeeded; however, the Bahamas are becoming a much less important source of fresh vegetables for the United States. Potatoes account for most of the U.S. imports from Canada.

18. Arthur B. Mackie, An Appraisal of Agricultural Export Potentials for Panama, USAID, Panama, February 1972.
19. G. Lindahl, Observations on Panamanian Agriculture, USAID, Panama, January 1969.

The demand for vegetables in the United States is expected to grow slowly during 1970–80. Per capita consumption is projected to remain at about the 1970 level. The structure of demand for vegetables changed substantially during 1960–70. Per capita consumption of canned and frozen vegetables increased while that of fresh vegetables declined. The decline in consumption of fresh vegetables is explained partly by changes in eating habits and partly by the rapid increase in the price of fresh vegetables compared to processed vegetables. The fresh produce industry has not mechanized and streamlined harvesting, handling, and marketing operations as much as the processing sector.[20]

Panama's ability to profitably export vegetables to the United States depends on delivery of top-quality products at costs no higher than those for Mexican produce. This task is likely to be difficult. Mexico has a 15 to 20 year head start and appears to be permanently established as the leading source of most warm-season vegetables that could be produced on a relatively large scale in Panama. Mexico's location assures it a transportation cost advantage to most sections of the U.S. market. Mexican labor costs, however, have been increasing and are expected to increase further, and such cost increases could help offset the transportation cost differential between Mexico and Panama.

The potential demand from tourists and high-income consumers in Panama City and the Canal Zone is great enough to absorb large quantities of top-quality fruits and vegetables. Rather than promoting exports, it would be more appropriate to concentrate on developing the potential of the domestic market.

Bananas

Bananas are Panama's most important export. In 1970, they accounted for over 57% of total exports of domestically produced products. The value of banana exports nearly tripled between 1960 and 1965 and then doubled between 1965 and 1970, increasing from B/11,640,100 in 1960 to B/60,831,300 in 1970.

Bocas del Toro province is the main banana-producing area. Most of the bananas exported are produced by the Chiriqui Land Company, which is a subsidiary of the United Fruit Company. The Chiriqui Land Company owns approximately 52,000 hectares of land. In 1970, its payroll was over B/22 million, its purchases of supplies and services amounted to B/18,817,000, and it paid B/3,281,000 in taxes. It is estimated that the company invested approximately B/29 million in its agricultural operations during the 1968–70 period.[21]

20. Charles W. Porter, The Vegetable Industry—A Review of Progress and Prospects, USDA, August 1970.
21. Chiriqui Land Company, Hechos acerca del Negocio del Banano en Panamá, 1971.

The Chiriqui Land Company was forced to take large amounts of land out of production during the 1950s in order to control the Panama disease in bananas. This disease spreads through the soil, attacks the root systems of plants, and eventually destroys them. Until the late 1950s, the two main methods of controlling Panama disease were flood flow programs or simple abandonment of diseased lands. The Gros Michael variety of banana, which was popular with consumers during the 1950s, was very susceptible to Panama disease.

The Valery banana, a highly disease-resistant variety, was developed through research in the late 1950s. Large plantings of this variety were begun in 1963 and, as a result, the late 1960s were good years for the world's banana producers. Production costs were lowered, and at the same time the international markets for bananas were extended as per capita consumption of bananas increased in Europe and Japan.

The 1970s are expected to be problem years for the world's banana producers. The world supply of bananas in 1974 has been projected to be 10,489,000 metric tons with demand estimated to be 6,384,000 tons. The abundant supply has resulted in lower prices for exported bananas, and further price declines are expected. The Chiriqui Land Company estimated that banana exports could be as high as 980,000 tons by 1974.[22] If exports continue to increase at about the same rate as during the 1960s, however, banana exports in 1974 would be approximately 725,000 tons or about 20% above the 1970 level. Export earnings from bananas are expected to increase more slowly as a result of expected price declines.

Long-run projections of the supply and demand for bananas require a great many assumptions about consumer tastes, trade policies, and production technology. Per capita consumption of bananas in importing countries is closely related to income but generally levels off at about 8 to 10 kilograms per year. Per capita consumption in producing countries varies widely, ranging from about 20 to over 40 kilograms. Supply adjustments require about 18 months.

The USDA has estimated that world prices could be maintained at about 1964–66 levels if banana exports (and imports) were increased at a rate of between 2% and 3% per year.[23] Assuming constant prices, the equilibrium quantity of world exports (and imports) in 1980 is estimated to be 6,515,000 metric tons.

The FAO projections of export availabilities indicate that world exports of bananas will be 7,797,000 metric tons by 1980. If this projection is correct, world import prices can be expected to fall by 30% to 40%, and export earnings would decrease by 18% to 24%. The FAO projection of Panama's 1980 export availabilities is 574,000 tons, which

22. Chiriqui Land Company, 1971.
23. USDA, World Demand Prospects for Bananas in 1980, Foreign Agricultural Economic Report 69, Washington, D.C., 1971.

is lower than the existing level.[24] The FAO projection, however, is based on the assumption that Panama will have the same share of world exports in 1980 that it had during the 1963–67 period.

The supply and demand situation projected for the 1970s implies that the successful competitors for shares of the world market must strive for lower production costs through less waste and more efficient distribution of high-quality exportable fruit. Assuming that banana exports will continue to increase as they did during the 1960s, total exports would be 760,000 metric tons in 1975 and 948,000 tons in 1980. If world import prices were to decline by 10%, export earnings from bananas would increase to about B/69 million in 1975 and to B/86 million in 1980. These are the projected values of banana exports under the most optimistic assumptions.

Projecting Panama's banana exports on the basis of past trends, with only a 10% price reduction, does not appear to be entirely justified in light of the world supply situation. Panama provided about 7% of the world's banana exports during the 1964–66 period. If Panama is able to increase its world market share to 10% by 1980 and world exports are held equal to the USDA equilibrium projections of 6,515,000 metric tons, Panama would export about 650,000 tons of bananas in 1980 and would earn about B/66 million at 1970 prices. If FAO projections for 1980 are used, Panama would export 779,000 tons in 1980 but would earn only B/62,376,000 if prices fell by 20%.

In summary, it appears unlikely that foreign exchange earnings from banana exports will continue to grow as rapidly during the 1970s as they did during the 1960s. World banana producers will either have to reduce the rate of increase in exports or accept substantial declines in world prices. The price declines, already evident in the early 1970s, are likely to lead to lower world exports by the late 1970s.

SUGAR

Sugarcane production is concentrated in the provinces of Cocle, Veraguas, and Herrera. Total production of cane in these provinces during the 1969–70 crop year exceeded 865,000 tons, which is approximately 86% of Panama's total production (Table 4.12). There were 17,700 hectares of sugarcane harvested in 1970. Total production was 1,009,200 tons, and the average yield was 57 tons per hectare. The survey of agricultural land resources indicates that only 15% of the land well suited for sugarcane production is presently being so used.

The average cost of production, including harvesting and transportation to the mill, is estimated to be approximately B/600 per hectare.[25]

24. FAO, Agricultural Commodities—Projections for 1975 and 1985, Vols. I and II, Rome, 1967.
25. A. Quiróz, Caña de Azúcar y Azúcar de Caña, SSC, Panama, April 1972.

TABLE 4.12. ● SUGARCANE PRODUCTION, 1969–70

Province	Area 000 ha	Area %	Production 000 tons	Production %	Yield (tons/ha)
Cocle	8.2	46.4	577.4	57.2	70.4
Veraguas	3.6	20.3	147.4	14.6	40.9
Herrera	3.4	19.2	140.9	14.0	41.4
Chiriqui	1.2	6.8	91.2	9.0	76.4
Los Santos	1.0	5.6	42.8	4.2	42.8
Others	0.3	1.7	9.5	1.0	31.7
Total	17.7	100.0	1,009.2	100.0	57.0

Source: Quiróz, 1972.

The production cost per ton of cane varies from B/8.50 to B/15 in the main producing provinces. Assuming an average yield of 1 ton of raw sugar for every 10 tons of cane, the raw material cost of raw sugar is estimated to be between B/85 and B/150 per ton. The 1970 FOB value of exports per ton of raw sugar was B/155. Therefore, there is very little margin to cover processing costs in areas where average yields are below 50 tons of cane per hectare. The U.S. quota price of raw (crude) sugar is approximately B/170. The free-market price has usually been considerably less than this. At the normal free-market world prices, the Panamanian sugar industry would not be profitable.

It is estimated that approximately 70% of the cane is processed by the nation's three largest mills. The output of these mills during 1974 is programmed to be 138,000 tons of sugar. This is divided as follows:

MILL	OUTPUT OF SUGAR IN 1974 (000 TONS)
Santa Rosa	45
Ofelina	54
La Victoria	39
Total	138

The newest mill, La Victoria, is owned and operated by the government and began operation in early 1973.

The linear trend projection of 1974 is 94,000 tons of sugar, but this does not take into account the potential output of the La Victoria mill. If the programmed output of 138,000 for 1974 is achieved, considerable amounts of sugar will have to be held in inventory or sold at free market prices. Either alternative will be costly.

Panama's U.S. sugar quota doubled between 1967 and 1973. The 1973 quota was 69,330 tons. Panama would have to increase sugar output to 120,000 tons by 1975 to fill the U.S. quota and meet domestic demands. Total production of sugarcane would have to increase to approximately 1.5 million tons, nearly 50% above the 1970 output. This jump is technically feasible, but increasing production beyond this point is unlikely to be profitable unless the U.S. sugar quota is increased.

If Panama were able to increase annual sugar exports by 30,000 tons at B/170 per ton, foreign exchange earnings would increase by B/5.1 million. Growth of sugar exports would help reduce the impact of the expected reduced rate of growth in foreign exchange earnings from bananas.

The linear trend projections of supply and demand shown in Table 4.13 are based on 1960–70 data. The linear trend production projections for 1975 are too low because they do not take account of the new plant opened in 1973. The SSC 1975 production projection, on the other hand, appears to be overly optimistic. The linear trend and the SSC projections of domestic consumption in 1975 are nearly identical. Using the average of the two sets of projections, nearly 79,000 tons of sugar would be available for export in 1975. If the U.S. export quota remains at the present level, it would be necessary to sell approximately 10,000 tons of sugar at world market prices.

COFFEE

The coffee industry has been able to supply the domestic market and provide a small export surplus,[26] but production possibly will be insufficient to meet domestic needs by 1975. Total coffee production in 1970 was 5,200 tons, of which 1,600 tons were exported. Coffee production is projected to increase slightly to about 5,500 tons by 1975. The projected domestic consumption is expected to be in the range of 4,600 to 7,000 tons (Table 4.13). Using the low consumption projection, total coffee exports would be 900 tons in 1975.

Some coffee is produced in all provinces, but most of the commercial coffee producers are located in Chiriqui province. In all other provinces, coffee is produced on very small farms by producers whose primary concern is the cultivation of food crops for their own consumption. These producers do not use improved varieties or modern cultural

---

26. This section is based on a review of the coffee situation by J. Phillip Rourke, USDA coffee consultant.

TABLE 4.13. • PROJECTED SUPPLY AND DEMAND BALANCES FOR SUGAR, COFFEE, AND BEVERAGES, 1975 AND 1980

Item	Production		Apparent Consumption		Surplus (Deficit)	
	1975	1980	1975	1980	1975	1980
Sugar (000 MT)						
a. Trend[a]	99.4	126.0	45.9	54.5	53.5	71.4
b. SSC[b]	148.0	n.a.	44.0	49.0	104.0	n.a.
c. Average	123.7	--	45.0	--	78.8	--
Coffee (000 MT)						
a. Trend[a]	5.5	5.8	4.6	5.2	0.9	0.6
b. SSC[c]	5.5	6.0	7.0	8.4	(1.5)	(2.6)
Beverages (000 hl)						
a. Nonalcoholic	712	897	712	897	--	--
b. Alcoholic	63	78	66	79	(3)	(1)
c. Beer	429	499	431	504	(2)	(5)

[a]Based on 1960-70 data.

[b]Quiróz, 1972.

[c]Major projections made by the SSC are in Hoffmann, 1971

practices. Average yields outside the province of Chiriqui are estimated to be only 250 pounds per hectare. At these yield levels, coffee is not a commercially profitable proposition. This type of production can continue only because the farmer hires no outside labor, uses no purchased inputs, and assigns a zero opportunity cost to the labor provided by his family and himself. Area planted in coffee in provinces other than Chiriqui declined from 17,500 hectares in 1963 to 15,800 in 1970, and further declines are expected. Farmers have shown very little interest in the government's program to provide coffee seedlings at the modest price of B/0.10 per tree.

The province of Chiriqui has good coffee soils located at the high altitudes necessary for production of quality coffee. A number of farmers in this area produce 100 to 250 quintals annually, and they obtain average yields of 7 quintals per hectare. Although more than double the yields in the other provinces, this level is still well below that at which coffee can be considered a profitable enterprise in Latin America.

Between 1963 and 1970, the land area devoted to coffee in Chiriqui province increased from 8,700 to 9,400 hectares. Some of this increase was near the border of Costa Rica where new road construction and the government's agricultural development programs have generated interest in coffee production.

Modernization of the coffee industry would require a radical departure from the way coffee has been produced traditionally. It would be necessary to adopt a complete package of technological innovations to modernize the industry. Among the more important necessary changes are (1) introduction of new varieties such as Caturra, Bourbon, and Mundo Novo to replace the widely used Arabica Tipica variety; (2) increased planting density; (3) increased fertilization rates; (4) introduction of modern pruning techniques and disease control procedures; and (5) reduction of shade. Implementing such a technological package could increase yields in Chiriqui province to 15 to 20 quintals per hectare.

Most small farmers elsewhere in Panama probably lack the managerial sophistication needed to implement such a program successfully. Substantial amounts of long-term investment capital would be needed by the larger farmers in Chiriqui province in order to implement the program. The cost of hired labor has increased steadily. This trend is expected to continue, and it is likely to become increasingly difficult to find the number of laborers needed during the harvest season. Large producers probably will consider the labor situation carefully when estimating the expected returns on a modernization program.

In brief, while it would be technically feasible to modernize Panama's coffee industry, at least in Chiriqui province, the difficulties are great enough that it is doubtful that a large government-sponsored modernization program would be successful. An alternative approach would be to provide a small amount of long-term investment capital to producers in Chiriqui province who are interested in bringing new land into coffee production or in introducing new varieties and production techniques on existing coffee lands. Bringing 2,000 to 3,000 hectares of new coffee land into production within 1970–80 should be adequate to avoid the possibility of having to import a relatively large percentage of the coffee required during the 1980s.

SUMMARY AND IMPLICATIONS

The supply and demand projections prepared by the SSC in early 1971 indicated that by 1975 the domestic production of nearly all major food products except beef, coffee, and bananas would be less than domestic demand. These projections also suggested that the supply deficits for most major foods would increase further by 1980 unless major efforts were made to increase agricultural production. The short-run implications of these projections are obvious. Panama must increase food imports if food prices are to be maintained, or prices will have to increase if domestic supply and demand are to be equated without increased imports.

Both approaches were used during the 1960s; for some products, imports were increased, while for others, prices were allowed to adjust upward. The alternative of rapidly increasing agricultural production could not be implemented in the late 1960s for several reasons. Investment opportunities outside agriculture were more attractive to large landowners than the opportunities available within agriculture. Secondly, the government did not have enough well-trained technicians or "technology packages" to rapidly increase the productivity of small and medium farmers. This situation has not changed. The asentamiento program can be viewed as an attempt to concentrate the government's limited resources to assist small farmers through the use of large-farm technology which is feasible for those products where it is significantly more productive than small-farm technology. Rice is a possible example. There is little evidence to suggest that the existing large farms are significantly more efficient than small farms in the production of products such as cattle, corn, beans, or vegetables. If, in fact, they are not more efficient, the formation of asentamientos will not increase production significantly until new technology suited for this form of resource control can be developed and introduced. Time is required for this type of development. Indeed, one might expect any large-scale government-sponsored development programs for agriculture to require at least a year or two to plan and finance and another three to five years or more to implement.

The trend projections of supply discussed in this chapter are not significantly different from SSC projections. The trend projections of demand frequently are somewhat below SSC projections due to differences in the statistical techniques used. Nevertheless, both sets of projections lead to basically the same conclusions. Retail food prices and imports are likely to continue to increase more rapidly during the early 1970s than they did during the 1960s. The upward pressures on food prices and imports are expected to continue during the last half of the decade, unless aggressive government actions are taken to increase the productivity of land, labor, and capital presently employed in agriculture; increase the amount of land in farms; and encourage a higher rate of investment in the agricultural sector.

No single program or action is "best" or will provide the "solution" to the problem of food supply deficits. Programs must be designed that take into account differences in geographical regions as well as differences in products and types of producers raising various products. Sorghum production, for example, probably can be increased most readily through price support programs and by providing rice farmers with technical information and varieties well suited to their regions. Government-sponsored irrigation and water control programs could have a substantial impact on rice production in some areas. Road construction programs may be the easiest way to increase cattle production in some parts of the country. Whether or not road construction is the "best" way in the long run will depend on the government's ability to implement land use policies that will maximize the nation's long-run benefits from the resources in the areas opened. The long-run value of the forestry resources in many new areas may be increased substantially by regulating the way trees are cut rather than allowing cattle producers and others to undertake "slash and burn" farming in new areas. In some regions, the "best" way to increase cattle production may be to concentrate on increasing the carrying capacity of pastures, while in other areas, the "best" approach may be to emphasize improvements in livestock management, better disease control, and supplemental feeding programs.

Supply and demand projections presented in this chapter suggest that the rapid rate of growth in earnings from agricultural exports experienced in the 1960s is unlikely to continue during the 1970s. The value of banana exports is expected to level off. The value of beef exports is unlikely to increase very much even though world beef prices may continue to rise, and Panama will have to restrict beef exports or allow domestic prices to increase. Coffee exports are projected to decline. Exports of sugar and seafood, on the other hand, are expected to increase. The increased earnings from sugar and seafood exports should be enough to keep total earnings from agricultural exports growing slightly, but not at 1960 rates. With regard to increasing sugar and seafood export earnings, uncertainty exists concerning how rapidly the new sugar mill will reach full-capacity production, whether or not the U.S. sugar quota will be changed, the speed with which new fishing boats will be constructed, and the magnitude of the seafood resources off the coasts of Panama.

Since agricultural exports, especially bananas, are so important as sources of export earnings, the expected decline in their growth rate has serious implications for the overall rate of growth in the economy. Growth in the 1970s cannot continue at the high rate of the 1960s in the absence of rapid growth in export earnings. This necessity intensifies the need for output-increasing policies and programs in agriculture so that exports can increase along with supplies for the domestic market.

CHAPTER FIVE

MARKETING
BASIC FOODS

THE SUPPLY AND DEMAND projections discussed in Chapter 4 indicated that Panama's food marketing system must be able to handle at least 20% to 25% more food during 1973–78. This will require sizable investments in storage, transportation, and food processing facilities. The government, through its price policies, import controls, and taxing powers, can play an important role in promoting and directing private investment in food marketing. The agricultural Sector Study Commission (SSC) limited its marketing studies to basic food grains, meat, milk, fruits, and vegetables as well as food retailing. These products account for over 80% of total consumption of basic foods and are likely to receive high priority in future market improvement programs.

Marketing middlemen add to the value of farm products through processing, transportation, and storage. Their performance can be judged by the composition of end results, which include the cost of marketing services, the availability of products at the time and place they are needed, the quality of the products, and the degree to which producers are provided with information about amounts of products needed in the future. Prices are an important factor in determining how well a market performs, and middlemen frequently can exert much direct or indirect control over prices.

Most food marketing is left to private individuals, but the government restricts their actions in many ways. It controls prices of nearly all major food items; regulates the importation and exports of many food items; enforces laws regulating milk and meat processing; sets minimum farm prices for rice and corn; and is actively involved in the storage, processing, and retailing of some food items, though generally on a small scale.

The government assists the food marketing sector in several ways. Product testing services are available for some food items. Price information is collected and distributed through a small market news program. Cold storage facilities that sell products to private retailers are operated by the government. The construction and maintenance of roads have helped reduce marketing costs.

The primary goal of official food price policies during 1960–70 appears to have been the maintenance of stable retail prices; this objective was achieved with remarkable success. The prices fixed by the government have at times favored consumers and at other times producers; but, in general, prices have been increased only when it appeared absolutely necessary to avoid substantial increases in imports of particular food items. In the past, the government has limited its direct marketing activities primarily to storable products such as grains, potatoes, and onions. These operations usually have been part of price control programs rather than an effort to completely control the marketing of particular commodities.

Although the marketing channels are different for each class of foods, nearly all have one common characteristic. At some point in the market process a few wholesalers or processors control a large percentage of the total product. It seems that the government has used price controls primarily to regulate the power of the marketing oligopolies. Import controls and direct operation of marketing facilities have served as secondary regulatory instruments. Marketing channels do not appear to have become more competitive over time and seem unlikely to do so in the future. Both consumers and producers, therefore, are likely to continue to favor some type of government control over food prices.

GRAIN MARKETING

Grain is marketed through both private and government channels.[1]

Domestic producers sell to private merchants when farm prices are above support levels but deliver substantial quantities of grain to the government when free-market prices fall below support levels. In addition to its direct marketing functions, the government performs regulatory functions, including control of consumer prices of grain products, as well as performing service functions such as grain inspection and grading, research and education, and market news.

Rice millers dominate the private trade, controlling most of the commercial grain storage, milling, drying, and cleaning capacity, along with the marketing services for rice and milling by-products. Many of the larger milling companies also sell farm machinery, fertilizers, pesticides, and other inputs needed by rice producers. Local assembly functions are performed by the millers through agents or direct representatives and by local dealers and merchant truckers.

---

1. Much of the material in this section is based on Richard Phillips, Needs and Opportunities for Improved Grain Marketing in Panama during the Decade Ahead, Food and Feed Grain Institute, Kansas State University, Manhattan, October 1971.

The major consumer markets for grain products are in the provinces of Panama and Colon in the central section of the country, but the major production areas are located far from these areas. The largest and most rapidly growing grain production area is Chiriqui, the province that borders Costa Rica. No railroads serve the grain-producing areas, so that the grain must be transported by truck or ship. Most of the grain moving from the western provinces moves by truck, but shipments from Darien province must move by ship.

The general net physical distribution patterns for grain during 1969–70 can be constructed from the data shown in Table 4.6. For rice, the general flow is toward the centers of population, especially Panama City and Colon. In terms of rough rice, a total volume of 1,471,000 quintals moved into Panama province during 1969–70 of which 396,000 quintals were diverted to Colon. Of that amount, 97,000 quintals were sent to Bocas del Toro. Over one-half the total volume moving into Panama province (765,000 quintals) came from Chiriqui. This amount was supplemented by 236,000 quintals from Veraguas, 32,000 quintals from Los Santos, 35,000 quintals from Herrera, 259,000 quintals from Cocle, 68,000 quintals from Darien, and 76,000 quintals from local market points in Panama province.

A large portion of the rice crop is milled in the province where it is produced, so that the total tonnage actually transported probably is less than three-fourths of the rough rice tonnages. The major portion of Chiriqui rice, for example, is milled in that province, with most of the remainder moving to intermediate points in Veraguas and Cocle provinces for milling.

The flow patterns for corn follow the same general direction of those for rice. However, smaller volumes are involved, and corn usually moves over shorter distances. For example, in 1970, only 18.5% of the total volume of corn moving into Panama province came from Chiriqui, compared to 52% of the volume of rice.

The flow patterns for beans closely follow those for corn, except on a much smaller scale. Approximately 50% of the beans produced are marketed. Bean marketings in 1969–70 totaled only 54,900 quintals, compared to nearly 640,000 quintals of corn marketed.

In general, the improvement and expansion of grain marketing and processing facilities have kept pace with the expanding grain production. Total grain storage capacity at market points in 1970 was reported to be 1,876,700 quintals.[2]

Panama has no long-term grain storage reserve. Only normal seasonal supplies are carried over at the end of the year. Some of the total storage capacity is undoubtedly used for custom storage of grain reported for on-farm consumption and an additional amount for work space.

2. Latinoconsult Argentina, S.A., Programa de Asistencia Tecnica al Departamento de Fomento, Tomo 1, Aspectos Descriptivos, Panama, 1970.

TABLE 5.1. • GRAIN STORAGE CAPACITY AT TERMINAL POINTS (000 QUINTALS)

Type of Storage	Panama	Penonome	Santiago	Sona	David	Total
Government						
Bulk	80.0	5.0				85.0
Bag	35.0	80.0	10.0	0.4	100.0	225.4
Total	115.0	85.0	10.0	0.4	100.0	310.4
Private						
Bulk		100.0				100.0
Bag	145.0	185.0	120.0	200.0	545.0	1,195.0
Total	145.0	285.0	120.0	200.0	545.0	1,295.0
Combined						
Bulk	80.0	105.0				185.0
Bag	180.0	265.0	130.0	200.4	645.0	1,420.4
Total	260.0	370.0	130.0	200.4	645.0	1,605.4

Source: Phillips, 1971.

Still, with staggered harvesting and two crops per year, efficient operators should be able to achieve an annual storage turnover of at least 2.0. Thus if the storage facilities are located properly and designed and in condition for effective utilization, a total of 1.5 million quintals of storage capacity would be ample for present (1974) grain marketing volumes.

Panama also had ample rice milling capacity to meet 1974 requirements. Accurate figures on milling capacity by type and location are not available, but the milling industry is competitive and has continued to upgrade and expand capacity. Many of the mills operate on a 24-hour basis during the harvest season, but overall mill capacity is not fully utilized on a year-round basis. The government rice mills are maintained largely on a standby basis and are used primarily when market prices drop to support levels.

The grain storage capacity by type and ownership at the five terminal markets is shown in Table 5.1. The bulk capacity is metal silo construction. The bag capacity is in flat warehouses, mostly of steel and masonry construction. About 40% of the total terminal grain storage capacity is located in David and another 23% in Penonome. All the capacity at David, Santiago, and Sona is bag storage. The government distribution elevator in Panama City and the private rice mill holding bins at Penonome account for most of the bulk storage. The total storage capacity at the five terminal points represents 86% of the total existing grain storage.

It is estimated that there is an additional 271,300 quintals of commercial grain storage capacity at country points outside the five terminal markets. This capacity is located in smaller towns throughout the grain-producing regions and is used primarily for assembling, conditioning, and holding grain as it moves from the farms. Nearly all the grain storage capacity at country points is flat storage for bagged grain.

Both government and private grain merchants operate buying offices in the smaller towns and villages throughout the grain production areas. Grain may be assembled into truckload lots at these buying station points, or it may be transported directly from the farm to the nearest country or terminal point for conditioning, storage, and processing.

Reliable figures are not available for total on-farm grain storage capacity, but it appears that substantial quantities of grain are stored on the farm. In 1969–70, for example, a total of 1,731,400 quintals of rough rice, 1,289,300 quintals of corn, and 54,610 quintals of edible beans were maintained on farms for home consumption. Much of the grain stored on farms is produced by small farmers who air-dry it in the sun or in open sheds before threshing or husking and then store it in their homes or adjoining structures, milling it by hand or at local custom mills as needed. Few small farmers have proper grain storage facilities, and most incur substantial storage losses from rodents, insects, and mold. Some medium farmers store their grain in facilities owned by local cooperatives. A few of the large, commercial farms are installing their own mechanical drying and steel bin storage facilities and, in some cases, rice milling machinery. Such facilities still are very limited, however, even in the commercial rice growing areas.

Several types of government programs have a major impact on grain production and marketing. Most of these programs and policies are being revised continuously in response to current problems and needs. The following is a brief review of the major programs in effect in 1973.

Government Programs

PRICE SUPPORTS AND CONTROLS. Panama has maintained the farm prices of rice, corn, and edible beans at levels above world market prices in order to support farm incomes and encourage increased production. Prices of these products also are controlled at the retail level. The farm price supports are maintained by accepting delivery of grains from producers at the announced price support levels. The retail price controls are maintained by government sales of domestic and imported grain.

GRAIN IMPORT POLICIES. All grain imports are made directly by the government. Because domestic prices are substantially above world market prices, the import operation provides a major source of revenue to support the total price stabilization and marketing operations of the government.

Government policy has been to keep grain imports at minimum levels. Rice is imported only when studies of rice stocks in all positions indicate definite approaching shortages. Corn is imported only when essential to supply food and processing industry demands. This policy has served to ration available supplies of domestic grain and to hold retail prices close to the legal maximums. In the case of the poultry and livestock feed industry, government policies have caused maximum substitution of rice bran, wheat by-products, and other ingredients for corn in formula feeds.

RESEARCH AND EDUCATIONAL PROGRAMS. Many of the research and educational programs affecting grain production and marketing are strongly oriented toward rice rather than corn or edible beans. Major programs affecting producers include crop breeding, fertilization, variety testing, pest control, and demonstration programs carried out at the agricultural experiment stations. In addition, detailed cost of production studies are conducted on a continuing basis.

Marketing research and education include studies of milling performance and techniques for different rice varieties, educational programs on quality testing and grading, and other technical aspects of grain processing and marketing. The total impact of the research and educational programs is difficult to measure, but it seems clear that they have been a major factor in achieving increased yields and production of rice and corn.[3]

GRAIN GRADING AND INSPECTION. Under the existing price support program, Panama is developing a workable grain grading and inspection system. The government trains inspectors and provides inspection services and laboratory analyses to millers and private handlers who desire them. Although the private trade has been slow in shifting to the use of standard quality measurements when buying from producers, the change can be expected in time.

The dockage system for excessive moisture and foreign material, based on careful sample inspection of the grain, is practical in most production areas. Because grain is sold by weight, producers and handlers alike readily understand dockage for extra water and extraneous material in grain. The system encourages producers to harvest and handle the grain properly and rewards them for doing so.

---

3. The potential of research and educational programs for increasing grain production are discussed in greater detail in Charles Breitenbach, Development of an Action Program to Systematically Achieve an Expanded Production of Basic Cereal and Leguminous Grains in the Republic of Panama, AID, Panama, February 1973.

New Marketing Facilities Needed

Projected increases in the volumes of production and consumption of grain imply that expanded marketing facilities will be needed. Some of the existing facilities need remodeling and updating, but much of this renovation can be accomplished in the process of adding to the existing capacity. The needs for expansion and updating of the grain marketing facilities vary considerably from one province to another, both in magnitude and in the kinds of facilities needed to meet the projected requirements.

The summary of projected grain marketings and shipments by province shown in Table 5.2 forms the basis for projecting future requirements for marketing facilities. The figures in the table show the estimated total marketings and shipments of all three grains for 1970 and the projected levels for 1975 and 1980.[4] The marketings and shipments of rice are in rough rice equivalent; those of corn and edible beans are on a shelled basis.

The indicated marketing volumes in Section A of the table represent the projected total off-farm sales of grain produced in each province. For the country as a whole, marketings of the three grains are projected to reach 3,920,300 quintals by 1975 and 5,233,800 quintals by 1980. Most of the increase in marketings between 1970 and 1980 is projected to occur in Chiriqui (1,044,900 quintals), Veraguas (483,200 quintals), Cocle (45,800 quintals), Panama (292,800 quintals), and Darien (239,400 quintals).

The indicated shipments in Section B of Table 5.2 represent the projected net total annual volume of grain to be transported from the province to other areas or from other areas to the province. Except for imports, the total provincial outshipments and inshipments cancel out for the country as a whole so that the totals are zero. Provinces with major increases in projected outbound shipments over the 1970–80 period include Chiriqui (716,100 quintals), Veraguas (445,500 quintals), Darien (213,500 quintals), and Cocle (190,100 quintals). Those with major increases in projected inbound shipments include Panama (1,513,200 quintals), Colon (167,900 quintals), and Bocas del Toro (58,300 quintals).

NEED FOR ADDITIONAL STORAGE FACILITIES. The need for additional grain storage capacity depends largely upon the average total storage

---

4. The data in Table 5.2 are based on the supply and demand projections prepared by the Food and Feed Grain Institute in 1971. The estimates prepared by the Institute in 1973 suggest that Panama has the potential to substantially increase the production of grain sorghum. The potential increase in sorghum production is not taken into account in the estimates of grain storage capacity discussed in this section.

TABLE 5.2. • SUMMARY OF PROJECTED GRAIN MARKETINGS AND SHIPMENTS BY PROVINCE, 1970, 1975, AND 1980 (000 QUIN-TALS)

Item	Bocas del Toro	Chiriqui	Veraguas	Herrera	Los Santos	Cocle	Panama	Colon	Darien	Country Total
A. Marketings										
1. 1970										
a. Rice	5.4	1,093.5	236.0	35.1	31.9	359.9	48.1	11.7	90.0	1,911.6
b. Corn	2.0	207.0	154.9	65.9	44.9	11.8	54.3	15.5	83.5	639.8
c. Beans	0.3	20.0	22.1	1.0	1.8	3.3	2.6	0.5	3.3	54.9
d. Total	7.7	1,320.5	413.0	102.0	78.6	375.0	105.0	27.7	176.8	2,606.3
2. 1975										
a. Rice	7.7	1,414.5	395.8	70.9	31.9	449.7	157.2	38.0	180.9	2,746.6
b. Corn	3.7	338.4	221.8	68.0	96.4	66.2	146.7	26.1	136.0	1,103.3
c. Beans	0.4	14.9	40.2	1.0	1.8	5.3	2.7	0.8	3.3	70.4
d. Total	11.8	1,767.8	657.8	139.9	130.1	521.2	306.6	64.9	320.2	3,920.3
3. 1980										
a. Rice	7.7	1,918.9	553.4	90.1	31.9	600.4	175.1	46.5	244.5	3,668.5
b. Corn	5.1	436.0	299.2	81.3	138.2	115.0	219.6	32.4	168.4	1,495.2
c. Beans	0.4	10.5	43.6	1.0	1.8	5.4	3.1	1.0	3.3	70.1
d. Total	13.2	2,365.4	896.2	172.4	171.9	720.8	397.8	79.9	416.2	5,233.8

TABLE 5.2. ● **(CONTINUED)**

	Bocas del Toro	Chiriqui	Veraguas	Herrera	Los Santos	Cocle	Panama	Colon	Darien	Country Total
B. Shipments										
1. 1970										
a. Rice	-97.4	765.2	236.0	35.1	31.9	258.6	-1,010.4	-286.5	67.5	0.0
b. Corn	-23.7	114.2	154.9	54.2	41.3	-12.6	-368.2	-78.3	68.2	-50.0
c. Beans	-3.0	13.2	22.1	1.0	1.8	-1.6	-28.3	-7.8	2.6	0.0
d. Total	-124.1	892.6	413.0	90.3	75.0	258.6/-14.2	-1,406.9	-372.6	138.3	-50.0
2. 1975										
a. Rice	-114.9	993.5	395.8	70.9	31.9	313.1	-1,513.2	-327.5	150.4	0.0
b. Corn	-34.8	164.5	209.8	39.8	79.2	3.8	-511.5	-112.3	114.7	-46.8
c. Beans	-3.1	3.9	40.2	0.3	1.4	-0.8	-42.0	-9.3	2.4	-7.0
d. Total	-152.8	1,161.9	645.8	111.0	112.5	316.9/-0.8	-2,066.7	-449.1	267.5	-53.8
3. 1980										
a. Rice	-135.6	1,402.1	553.4	74.1	31.9	425.1	-2,167.8	-389.5	206.3	0.0
b. Corn	-43.1	206.6	261.5	39.9	114.3	23.6	-691.3	-139.8	143.3	-85.0
c. Beans	-3.7	-4.6	43.6	-0.5	1.1	-2.0	-61.0	-11.2	2.2	-36.1
d. Total	-182.4	1,608.7/-4.6	858.5	114.0/-0.5	147.3	448.7/-2.0	-2,920.1	-540.5	351.8	-121.1

Source: Phillips, 1971.

turnover rate that can be expected in the future. The total turn-over depends upon harvesting patterns, the year-end carryover, and the number of different facilities within the total system through which the grain moves on its way to the ultimate consumer. It also depends upon the effectiveness with which the various storage facilities in the system can be utilized. For example, if government storage facilities are utilized only for grain delivered under the price support program, the average total utilization will be relatively low in years when market prices to farmers remain above support prices. However, if the government facilities can be leased to private handlers when not needed for receiving grain delivered under the support program, the average total utilization of storage capacity will be relatively high.

The average storage turnover of grain in private and government storage facilities in 1969–70 was approximately 1.5. If the storage facilities are located properly and utilized effectively, turnover rates with future increased marketing volumes can be slightly higher than those achieved in 1969–70. With regard to distribution facilities, since one month's supply in the consumption centers is adequate to ensure orderly marketings, an annual turnover of 12.0 is used as the standard. In the case of grain storage facilities at processing and shipment points (including both country and terminal facilities), an average total annual turn-over of about 2.0 is indicated for an orderly marketing system. Individual marketing units should be able to achieve a turnover of 2.5 for rice storage and 4.0 for corn storage. It should be pointed out that the aggregate annual average turnover will not be as high as the turnover for individual units because some of the grain will move through two or more facilities within the marketing system (e.g., from a country storage unit to a terminal storage unit).

The projected grain storage capacity requirements for 1975 and 1980 are shown in Table 5.3. The "additional capacity needed" is obtained by subtracting the existing private storage capacity in 1970 from the projected "total capacity needed" in 1975 and 1980. The "additional capacity needed with 80% of GOP [Government of Panama]" is the amount of new storage capacity that would be needed if 80% of the government's storage capacity were utilized, either by leasing government facilities to private operators or by storing grain purchased as part of the government's price support program. Leasing 80% of the government's grain storage capacity to private operators would reduce the amount of new capacity needed in 1975 by 25% and that needed in 1980 by 20%. The remaining 20% would still provide some standby capacity if farm prices should drop below support levels.

A leasing program could result in substantial savings in the capital outlay for new facilities and in improved operating efficiency of the marketing system as a whole without loss of the benefits from a farm price support program. The total additional grain storage capacity

TABLE 5.3. ● PROJECTED GRAIN STORAGE CAPACITY BY PROVINCE, 1975 AND 1980 (000 QUINTALS)

Province	Total Capacity Needed		Additional Capacity Needed		Additional Capacity Needed with 80% of GOP	
	1975	1980	1975	1980	1975	1980
Bocas del Toro	16	18	14	16	13	15
Chiriqui	884	1,183	273	572	189	488
Veraguas	329	448	0	68	0	60
Herrera	70	86	13	29	13	29
Los Santos	65	86	39	60	39	60
Cocle	260	360	0	67	0	0
Panama	281	379	104	202	32[a]	127[a]
Colon	61	74	61	74	61	74
Darien	160	208	150	198	146	194
Total	2,126	2,842	654	1,286	493	1,047

Source: Phillips, 1971.

[a]Based on the assumption that only 60% of the government's distribution facilities in Panama City are available for leasing in years when limited amounts of grain are purchased under the price support programs.

needed by 1975 is 654,000 quintals without the leasing program and 493,000 quintals with the leasing program. Chiriqui province needs nearly 42% of the projected 1975 additional storage requirements. If the highway under construction to the rice production areas of Darien province is not completed, much of the additional capacity indicated for this province will have to be located in Panama province instead. If the government's program to encourage grain sorghum production is successful, additional storage capacity will be needed in some provinces, especially Chiriqui and Panama.

The type, number, and size of the additional storage facilities for an improved total marketing system vary by province. The best configuration for each province depends upon the existing facilities; the total additional capacity needed to meet projected requirements; the relative mix of rice, corn, and beans used in determining the projected requirements; the average size and type of grain producers in the area; the adequacy of farm-to-market roads; and the ultimate destination of the grain marketed in the area. Bocas del Toro, for example, needs small country storage units should be incorporated with small rice mills and supporting facilities in the city of Bocas del Toro for handling shipped-in grain. Because the projected additional volumes and storage capacities are relatively small in both cases, simple low-cost structures are indicated. Rice dominates the determination of storage requirements, so that country storage units should be incorporated with small rice mills and supporting cleaning and drying equipment. These country units should be flat storage structures for receiving and handling grain in sacks.

In contrast to Bocas del Toro, the Chiriqui area is characterized by relatively large mechanized farms and rapidly expanding surplus production of rice. There are a number of mills in the area, all of which have facilities for storage of both rough and milled rice and for drying and cleaning the grain. Farm-to-market roads are adequate, and marketing costs can be reduced by converting from sacks to bulk handling directly from the farm. Bulk handling of rice already is working effectively in the Penonome area of Cocle province. Silo storage would best meet the projected requirements at both country and terminal locations in Chiriqui province. Terminal facilities should be designed for handling milled rice and cleaned and dried corn on pallets or belt conveyors for efficient loading to trucks for outbound shipments. Approximately four additional country facilities and five additional terminal facilities will be needed in Chiriqui by 1980. Some or all of these may represent remodeling of and additions to existing rice mills in the area.

ADDITIONAL MILLING CAPACITY NEEDED. It is estimated that Panama will need an additional 44 metric tons per hour of rice milling capacity by 1980.[5] This estimate includes 25 tons per hour of replacement capacity and 19 tons per hour of new capacity. Some of the additional rice mills will be needed at government facilities, but most will be needed by the private grain dealers.

ADDITIONAL CLEANING AND DRYING FACILITIES. An estimated 95 metric tons per hour of new cleaning and drying capacity will be needed by 1980 to handle the projected increases in marketings of rice, corn, and grain sorghum. Another 63 tons per hour will be needed to replace existing equipment; again, most of the new facilities will be needed by the private sector.

---

5. Phillips, 1971.

TRANSPORTATION FACILITIES. The trucking industry will have to make an
estimated net investment of about 6 new 10-ton, long-haul rigs and
and 13 new 2.5-ton trucks for farm-to-market hauls each year in
order to handle the projected increases in grain marketings.

ESTIMATED COSTS OF NEW MARKETING FACILITIES. The total cost of the new
grain marketing facilities needed during the 1970s is as follows:

Grain storage facilities	B/1,477,500
Rice milling facilities	1,114,700
Cleaning and drying facilities	450,400
Subtotal	3,042,600
Grain trucks	2,948,600
Total	B/5,991,200

These cost estimates include no provision for additional infrastructure
such as office buildings, educational facilities, and roads. The estimates
should be considered the minimum amounts necessary to obtain the facilities needed, assuming that funds are used wisely and effectively. The
estimates indicate that Panama must invest approximately B/600,000
annually in grain marketing facilities in order to handle the expected
increases in production.

Grain Prices and Marketing Margins

Prices of rice, corn, and edible beans are supported at the farm level
and controlled at the retail level by government policy. The price
support levels are uniform in all provinces with no adjustment for trans-
port cost to the consuming markets. They are uniform through time
from harvest until the next planting season, with no adjustment for
storage costs. They are uniform by class of grain except for differentials
made in the support levels for four classes of rice (extra long grain,
long grain, medium grain, and short grain) which began in the 1970–71
marketing year. No distinction is made between dent and flint corn
classes. Differentials for quality in the support levels are made by applying dockage scales for excess moisture and foreign material content
to rice and corn and by applying price discount scales for excess moisture, foreign material, and admixture of other classes to edible beans.
In addition, the support price for rice depends upon milling quality in
terms of the percentages of sound kernels, broken kernels, and "points."
The classification and grading system used under the price support program is more refined than that customarily used for grain purchases from
farmers by the private trade.

The support price levels for rice have remained constant for a number of years with a maximum support price of B/6 per quintal. The milling quality provisions instituted in the rice supports in 1970–71 had the effect of slightly lowering the average support levels. The long-term trend in market prices paid to farmers for rice has been slightly downward.

The support price for corn was raised to B/4.25 per quintal in August of 1970 in an effort to stimulate increased production. With the increased market demand, particularly by the poultry industry, and the tight regulation of imports, the long-term trend in domestic corn prices received by farmers has been upward.

Support prices for edible beans have been maintaind at B/8 per quintal for frijoles and B/11 per quintal for porotos for some time. However, the long-term trend in market prices has been upward as demand continues to increase and supply continues to decrease.

Stability in support price levels and the past record of acceptance of delivery of large quantities of grain under the price support program allowed the support prices to function as forward prices. Farmers knew the support levels and had assurance that they would be effective at the time planting decisions were made.

SEASONAL PATTERNS IN MARKET PRICES. The seasonal and secular patterns in farm prices of rice, corn, and edible beans were analyzed by the SSC, using monthly price data from 1962 to 1970. Results of the SSC study are presented in Table 5.4. Rice and corn prices usually are lowest in October and highest in July, immediately before the start of the fall harvest. There is less seasonal variation in the farm price of edible beans than in the prices of rice and corn. Bean prices tend to be lowest in March at the peak of the spring harvest and highest in October.

During the 1962–70 period, the farm price of rice declined nearly B/0.01 per quintal per month on the average. The average price of No. 1 rough rice during this period was B/5.77 per quintal, while No. 2 rough rice sold for B/4.94 per quintal. The farm price of corn averaged B/3.64 per quintal and increased by B/0.0076 per quintal per month. Edible beans sold for B/9.98 per quintal and moved upward monthly by B/0.015 per quintal.

These average seasonal fluctuations in the prices received by farmers are significant, but they are not adequate to cover the full costs of storing rice and only barely adequate to cover the full costs of storing corn and edible beans through the production season. The average seasonal price rise for No. 1 rough rice from October to the following July is about B/0.059 per quintal per month. The full storage cost for rice, even in an efficient commercial operation, is at least B/0.10 per quintal per month. At 1% per month, the interest on the storage inventory alone is about B/0.05 per quintal per month. Thus, at the average sea-

TABLE 5.4. ● AVERAGE SEASONAL PATTERNS IN FARM PRICES FOR RICE, CORN, AND BEANS, 1962–70

Month and Parameter	Rough Rice		Corn	Edible Beans
	No. 1	No. 2		
(index as %)				
January	97.6	96.6	96.6	102.8
February	98.8	97.8	95.6	93.7
March	100.6	101.0	94.9	89.7
April	100.8	101.0	94.7	91.0
May	102.8	103.6	100.7	95.6
June	105.2	105.8	107.8	101.1
July	105.2	106.9	115.2	104.6
August	101.6	103.1	110.2	102.3
September	97.7	97.8	95.2	103.0
October	96.1	95.6	93.4	108.7
November	96.5	95.1	96.5	104.3
December	96.9	95.5	99.4	103.2
(prices in balboas)				
Average Price ($\overline{Y}$)	5.77	4.94	3.64	9.98
Trend in Monthly Price (b)	-0.0097	-0.0097	+0.0076	+0.0147

sonal price patterns prevailing in Panama, on-farm storage of rice is not profitable. Off-farm storage at milling points is profitable only because it permits more effective use of milling facilities throughout the year.

The average seasonal price rise for corn from October through March and from April through July is about B/0.069 per quintal per month. A properly timed commercial storage operation can cover full storage costs at the prevailing seasonal price patterns for corn, but on-farm storage is not profitable. Corn inventory carrying cost alone is at least B/0.04 per quintal per month.

The average seasonal rise in the price of edible beans from March through October is about B/0.27 per quintal per month. This increase should be adequate to cover full storage costs, even though the inventory carrying cost alone for edible beans is about B/0.10 per quintal per month. The average seasonal price for edible beans falls continuously from October through February, so that storage through this period cannot be justified.

The average seasonal price patterns for milled rice at the retail level show little relationship to the price patterns for rough rice at the farm level. The seasonally constant price ceiling has kept consumer prices from following normal seasonal patterns resulting from harvest cycles. Prices have remained so nearly constant at or near ceiling levels that seasonal patterns are obscured by the declining secular trend in rice prices.

GEOGRAPHICAL PRICE DIFFERENCES. The government's price support programs have tended to reduce geographical differences in grain prices, especially for rice. Most regional differences in grain prices may be attributed to differences in assembly and marketing costs. In the case of rice, the regional differences in price are seldom large enough to cover transportation cost differences from the production areas to the major consumption centers in Panama and Colon provinces.

MARKETING MARGINS. For the country as a whole, rice producers have received on the average about two-thirds of the consumers' expenditures on rice. The producer's relatively high share is explained partly by the scale of rice production and partly by the competitiveness of the rice milling industry in some areas.

Marketing margins on edible beans are relatively wide. Farmers generally receive about 45% of the consumers' expenditures on beans. Most of the beans are produced by relatively small farmers, so that local assembly costs are high. Additionally, small volumes increase the expense of handling methods; therefore, unit costs are relatively high at all steps in the marketing system.

Marketing margins for corn vary greatly between the portion channeled to poultry and livestock feed manufacturers and other industrial outlets and that channeled to retail food outlets. Farmers receive between 75% and 80% of the user's dollar for the portion channeled to industry but only about 60% of that channeled to human consumption.

EFFECTIVENESS OF PRICE SUPPORT PROGRAMS. The present price support program for rice seems to have proved effective in maintaining minimum prices to farmers and stimulating production. The efficiency of the marketing system for rice probably could be improved if the structure of rice price supports were refined to more accurately reflect differences in value due to place, time, and quality.

The price supports for corn have been less effective in stimulating increased production than have those for rice. It is too early to measure the production response that might be attributed to the recent increase in support prices for corn. Some response can be expected, but it appears that many farmers still find rice the more profitable crop and and will not make a significant shift to corn production. It seems probable that market prices for corn have not been the factor limiting increased corn production. Programs are needed to reduce the per quintal costs of corn production in order to make this crop more profitable to farmers and thereby stimulate increased production.

A major problem with higher support prices and higher market prices for corn is the depressing effect on the poultry and livestock industries. At 1972 world market prices, corn and other feed grains represented important and economic ingredients for poultry and livestock rations. When feed grains are available at reasonable cost, the poultry and livestock industries are stimulated to expand to meet growing demands for meat, eggs, and dairy products. When feed grains are high priced, poultry and livestock production costs are high, even though other ingredients are substituted in the ration as far as possible. When poultry and livestock production are forced to compete with human food outlets in demand for corn, the domestic poultry and livestock industries remain depressed and the needed meat, eggs, and dairy products must be imported.

There may be a relatively easy answer to Panama's dilemma in this respect. Flint corn is needed to supply the demand for human food; the flint varieties are adapted to cultivation by small producers. Yields are relatively low and costs of production high, but the human food market can support relatively high prices to cover the production costs. Price supports for flint corn at B/4.25 per quintal, or even higher, can be absorbed without serious adverse effect on the economy.

Dent corn, rather than flint corn, normally is the economic source of energy in poultry and livestock rations. The high-yielding dent corn hybrids are more suited to cultivation by the large mechanized producers than by the small farmers. Production management is more exacting than for the indigenous flint varieties. Mechanical harvesting, drying, and handling in bulk are desirable. Specialized grain storage facilities are needed on the farm or at nearby market points. When the production management and handling system is provided, the dent hybrids provide high yields and can be produced at a low cost per quintal. If these facilities are developed and the market assured, dent corn production can be profitable to Panama's larger farmers, with suitable soil and climatic conditions, at price support levels of B/3.50 per quintal or less.

Price supports for corn could be established to allow higher prices for flint corn than for dent corn. At the same time, separate research and education programs tailored to flint corn production by small farmers and dent corn production on large mechanized farms would help to bring about the desired production responses.

The retail ceiling prices on milled rice, corn, and edible beans have been reasonably effective. At existing levels, ceiling prices provide price protection to consumers and still enable efficient millers and handlers to cover costs. Some minor adjustments in the ceiling prices to reflect differences in harvesting patterns and storage and transportation costs would encourage grain merchants to increase storage capacity and help reduce seasonal market shortages. The ability of the government to maintain the existing ceiling prices will depend upon continued and substantial increases in national production of grains or an increase in imports.

MILK MARKETING

Milk marketing begins on the farm at milking time. How milk is handled on the farm determines its potential uses and affects the way it is marketed. The on-farm handling is influenced by the fact that over 90% of the milk produced comes from dual-purpose beef and dairy herds with its sale being a secondary and highly seasonal operation. When dairying is a secondary operation, less attention is given to the use of sanitary milking and handling procedures. As a result, nearly all milk from joint beef-dairy operations is sold as industrial grade or Grade B at best.

In 1970, there were roughly 4,000 dairy-breed cows on approximately 25 large, specialized dairy farms. Census data indicate that there were another 6,000 dairy breed cows, largely Holstein-Friesian and Brown Swiss, on smaller farms. The specialized dairy farms produced approximately 6 million liters or 8.5% of the 71 million liters produced. The production of cows on specialized dairy farms was more than double the national average of 2 liters per day. The entire herd milked was 98,450 cows, which is less than 8% of the total cattle population. The dual-purpose cattle are generally Cebu-Criollo crosses with some admixture of the specialized dairy breeds.[6]

The large, specialized dairy farms can justify investment in milk cooling equipment and other facilities necessary for proper milk handling. These farms can also be inspected frequently to ensure that they comply with government requirements for Grade A milk production, which is not the case with farms milking only a few low-producing cows once a day as part of a joint beef-dairy operation. Educational programs may encourage small producers to wash cows properly before milking, sterilize milk handling equipment, and control mastitis. How-

---

6. Charles P. Swett, Milk Production and Marketing in Panama, GOP report, December 1971.

ever, small-scale operations generally would not find it profitable to invest in cooling facilities and other equipment necessary for Grade A milk production. Under these conditions, the only method of increasing the production of Grade A milk is to encourage the expansion in size and number of specialized dairy farms, which would be accomplished most easily by allowing the farm price of Grade A milk to increase.

Total milk production has remained approximately constant since 1967, fluctuating around 71 million liters annually. The consistency of production may be partly due to the change in the relative prices of beef and milk during 1960–70. Given the predominance of dual-purpose herds, the relationship between milk and meat prices affects the allocation of milk between calf feeding and the off-farm market. In 1961, with milk at B/0.09 per liter and beef at B/0.145 per kilogram, 1.61 liters of milk were required to equal 1 kilogram of beef. By 1972, with milk at B/0.10 and beef at B/0.18, the ratio was 1.80 liters of milk to 1 kilogram of beef.[7]

Increasing the price of industrial grade milk would encourage farmers to market more milk rather than feeding it to calves. It seems unlikely, however, that price increases alone will have much impact on the technology of milk production. Extensive education programs on livestock management will be necessary if the average production per cow is to be increased. A study of the profitability of milk production in Central America prepared by the Inter-American Institute of Agricultural Sciences (IICA) in 1970 determined that the use of feed concentrates resulted in increased revenues of 3.5 times the cost of the concentrates. Investment in purebred cows resulted in rates of return on investment, ranging from nearly 8% to over 50%.[8] Purebred dairy cattle may not be appropriate for dual-purpose herds in Panama, but there are opportunities to promote the upgrading of herds, e.g., increased emphasis on dual-purpose dairy cows at livestock fairs, promotion of performance records for bulls, and expansion of artificial insemination programs. There appears to be general agreement that both better feeding and upgrading of herds would be profitable for even small-scale livestock operations. Milk processors could provide valuable assistance in programs to increase milk production, and they would benefit by increased utilization of their processing facilities.

Los Santos, Herrera, and Chiriqui provinces account for nearly three-fourths of Panama's total milk production and over 80% of the total sales of raw milk for the production of condensed, evaporated, and powdered milk. Most of the Grade A milk is produced in Panama and Chiriqui provinces (Table 5.5).

7. Louis F. Herrmann, Beef and Milk Production and Marketing in Panama, American Technical Assistance Corporation, Panama, December 1971.

8. Juan Antonio Aguirre, Economía, Tecnología, Rentabilidad de la Producción de Leche en los Trópicos de América Central, San Carlos, Costa Rica, IICA, San José, 1970.

TABLE 5.5. • MILK PRODUCTION AND SALES BY PROVINCE

Province	No. of Dairy Cows[a]	Milk Production[a] (000 liters)	Sales of Raw Milk for Processing[b] (000 liters)
Los Santos	35,600	25,309	9,328
Herrera	23,200	13,979	5,325
Chiriqui	22,300	13,263	6,475
Cocle	6,600	7,292	2,940
Panama	6,100	8,002	964
Veraguas	3,700	2,471	679
Colon	700	490	--
Bocas del Toro	200	227	--
Darien	50	21	--
Total	98,450	71,054	25,711

Source: Food Industries Development, Ltd., Milk Processing in the Republic of Panama, Haifa, Israel, December 1971.

[a]1970.

[b]Sales of raw milk for the production of condensed, evaporated, and powdered milk in 1969.

The distribution of fluid milk by various uses in 1969 is shown in Table 5.6. Producers sold approximately 30% of their milk for consumption as raw, unpasteurized milk. Slightly over 25% of total milk production was processed into evaporated and condensed milk. Over three-fourths of the evaporated and condensed milk was produced at the Nestle plant at Nata in Cocle province; most of the remainder was produced by Industrias Làcteas, S.A., which is Panama's largest milk company. Pasteurized milk accounted for 22% of total milk utilized. Industrias Lácteas, processed nearly 94% of all pasteurized milk. One company (Klim) processed 8.5% of total milk production into powdered whole milk. Manufactured cheese utilized slightly over 5% of total milk

TABLE 5.6. ● MILK BALANCE SHEET, 1969

Form of Utilization		Thousands of Liters	Percent
Raw Milk		23,367	30.5
Milk Processed into Evaporated and Condensed		19,317	25.3
Nestle	14,860		
Ind. Lácteas	3,475		
Unaccounted for	982		
Pasteurized Milk		17,000	22.2
Cia. Suprema	1,060		
Ind. Lácteas	15,900		
Ind. Unidas	40		
Milk Processed into Powdered Whole Milk		6,475	8.5
Klim	6,475		
Manufactured Cheese (Milk to Cheese Calculated at 8 to 1)		4,000	5.2
Home Consumption of Milk		3,200	4.2
Homemade Cheese		3,060	4.0
Milk in Ice Cream		57	0.1
Total		76,476	100.0

Source: Swett, 1971.

production. The remaining 8% was consumed by producers either as raw milk or was processed in the form of homemade cheese.

Industrias Lácteas, the principal supplier of pasteurized milk, purchased 24,603,800 liters of fresh raw milk in 1970 from over 1,000 milk producers. Only 23 of its suppliers produced Grade A milk; 5 of them were located in Panama province, 15 in Chiriqui, 1 in Colon, and 2 in Cocle. These producers delivered 5.4 million liters of Grade A milk. The remaining 19.2 million liters were received as industrial milk.

Grade A milk is picked up daily at the farm in Panama and Colon and delivered directly to the Industrias Lácteas processing plant. In other provinces, Grade A milk is first taken to receiving stations in Chiriqui, Chitre, or Chorrera and then transported daily to Panama City. Producers in Chiriqui province generally receive B/0.05 less per liter than producers in Panama province, a difference that covers additional collection and transportation costs. The company maintains a full-time veterinarian who inspects and gives technical advice and assistance to the 15 Grade A milk producers in Chiriqui.

Industrial milk is delivered to the Industrias Lácteas receiving stations without being precooled. All milk is cooled at 40° F at the collection stations and transported to Panama City in stainless steel tanks. The largest quantity of milk is received at the Chitre station.

In 1969, approximately 20% of the company's Grade A pasteurized milk was sold in the Canal Zone with most of the remainder sold in Panama City and nearby urban centers. Grade B pasteurized milk accounted for two-thirds of the company's total sales of pasteurized milk. The remainder of the company's raw milk was used for evaporated milk, powdered skim milk, ice cream mix, cheese, yogurt, and other milk drinks.

Of the 40,000 gallons of ice cream mix prepared monthly, Industrias Lácteas sold approximately 6,000 gallons to ice cream manufacturers (Dairy Queen, Tastee Freeze, and Tambal) and used the remainder to prepare its own ice cream. Powdered skim milk is used to replace whole milk in the ice cream formula during the dry season.

The company has plant capacity for pasteurizing over 27 million liters annually on a one-shift basis. In 1970, its pasteurizing facilities were operating at about 60% of this one-shift capacity. It had approximately 40 refrigerated trucks that made daily deliveries to retail stores and five trucks that made home deliveries.

In general, the milk processing industry in Panama can be described as an oligopoly with two dominant firms. Industrias Lácteas controls the distribution of most of the pasteurized milk, and Nestle controls most of the production of evaporated and condensed milk. In 1969, these companies handled 45% of the nation's total milk production and nearly three-fourths of all milk sold to commercial processing companies. Their market power is influenced by the government through price and import controls.

Panama appears to have adequate milk processing and pasteurizing facilities for the present and near future. Latinoconsult estimated that milk processing plants were operating at about 70% of their capacity during the peak production months.[9] The quality of most milk plant facilities reportedly is adequate, and the facilities appear to be appropriately located.

9. Latinoconsult Argentina, S.A., Programa de Desarrollo Ganadero, Estudio de Diagnóstico, Panama, November 1969.

The major milk marketing problem appears to be improper handling and lack of sanitation at nearly all points in the milk marketing process. A consumer survey in Panama City in 1972 indicated that 77% of the consumers would buy more milk if quality were improved.[10] Of the 350 families surveyed, 46% stated that the quality of milk was poor, did not have a good taste, and did not keep well. These complaints are not due to milk products standards, which are more than adequate. Based on existing standards, the milk sold in Panama City should be nearly the best in the nation; the problem lies in enforcement.

Independent testing of milk products carried out in 1972 confirmed consumers' opinions about the quality of milk products sold in Panama City. There was wide variation in the fat content of pasteurized milk. Samples tested ranged from 2.1% to 3.2% fat, even though the standards set by law specify a minimum of 3.5%. The bacteria counts on raw milk received at the dairy processing plant were extremely high in most cases, which can be attributed mainly to poor handling of the milk before it reaches the rural receiving plants. The bacteria counts of pasteurized milk were quite good, but the coliform counts in ice cream frequently were unsatisfactory.

The lack of sanitary milk handling starts at the farm. Cows are not properly washed before milking, farmers fail to check for mastitic milk, diseased cows are not separated from the herd, and cooling facilities frequently are not available, and even when they are, they are not used or properly maintained. Even the simplest practices such as the use of proper milk filters frequently are ignored.

The purchasing procedures followed by the processors can influence the way milk is handled on the farm. When milk is purchased by volume only with no consideration given for differences in fat or solids content, the producers are tempted to add water; there is considerable evidence that producers succumb to this temptation. No testing is done for abnormal milk; therefore, no action can be taken to identify farmers delivering milk from diseased cows. No testing is done for antibiotics of pesticides in the milk. As a result, it is difficult to discourage farmers from selling milk from cows being treated with antibiotics or to encourage them to exercise proper control in the selection and use of pesticides

The purchasing and handling procedures of the milk processors are influenced by the quality control procedures followed by the Ministry of Health. The ministry maintains at least one inspector in each milk pasteurizing plant and takes samples each week from each producer or tank truck of raw milk received at the plant. These samples are tested by the ministry laboratory for bacteria, coliform count, specific gravity,

10. Floyd E. Fenton, Quality and Standards for Milk in the Republic of Panama, USDA, Washington, D.C., August 1972.

and milk fat. Pasteurized products are also tested to check the adequacy of the pasteurization treatment.

Only three of the six major ice cream manufacturers in Panama City had inspectors in the plants in 1972, due to the lack of personnel and the limited capacity of the Ministry of Health laboratory facilities. Testing of dairy product samples is limited to the first three days of the work week, and only a limited number of samples are tested. This system does not provide sufficient flexibility for running follow-up tests immediately when necessary or for running routine tests at irregular intervals. No tests are run for sediment content on the raw or pasteurized milk.

Obviously, both public health officials and milk processors are placing their faith in the pasteurization process to provide pure milk for consumers. Improvement of the quality of milk products will require close cooperation of public health officials and processors in urban areas and between processors and field personnel of the Ministry of Agricultural Development (MIDA) in rural areas. Such cooperation could improve the average quality of approximately 60% of the milk marketed. Improving the average quality of the other 40% of the milk production, which is sold as raw milk or consumed on the farm, would require a farm-level education program, along with efforts by municipal officials in rural areas, to control the quality of raw milk sold by local distributors.

LIVESTOCK MARKETING

The 1971 census placed the total cattle population at 1,259,892.

The leading provinces were Chiriqui (376,656 head), Los Santos (275,559 head), Veraguas (212,881 head), Panama (130,918 head), and Herrera (128,828 head); these five provinces account for nearly 90% of the total cattle population (Table 5.7). Panama province has had a higher rate of growth in its cattle population during the past decade than any other province. Cattle numbers in Panama province increased by over 146% during the 1961–71 period, a rate of growth reflecting the movement of cattle producers into the Darien region.

Livestock are held on all sizes of farms. Data developed in 1970 indicated that farms smaller than 50 hectares accounted for 85% of total cattle farms and held 41% of the nation's cattle. Farms with 50 to 100 hectares held 21% of the cattle. Farms larger than 100 hectares accounted for approximately 5% of total cattle farms and accounted for the remaining 38% of the nation's herd.[11]

In general, specialized dairy and dual-purpose cattle are held on small to medium properties, while specialized beef enterprises are more often found in the medium to large category. It appears that a gradual shift away from dual-purpose cattle to strictly beef is taking place. The

TABLE 5.7. ● BEEF CATTLE BY PROVINCE

Province	Cenus of 1950	Cenus of 1961	Cenus of 1971	Percent Change 1961-71
Bocas del Toro	4,829	8,647	8,889	2.8
Cocle	57,395	71,230	98,649	38.5
Colon	7,286	9,712	19,478	100.6
Chiriqui	162,581	235,015	376,656	60.3
Darien	1,888	3,586	8,034	124.0
Herrera	80,707	90,350	128,828	42.6
Los Santos	117,622	159,166	275,559	73.1
Panama	29,630	53,179	130,918	146.2
Veraguas	108,085	132,102	212,881	61.1
Total	570,023	762,987	1,259,892	65.1

Source: Dirección de Estadística y Censo, Existencia de Ganado Vacuno en la República: Años 1961 a 1972, Contraloria General de la República, November 1972.

total number of cows milked dropped by about 40% between 1960 and 1970. On the other hand, average milk production per cow increased by roughly 80% during the same period.

Livestock slaughter increased from a total of 124,370 head in 1964 to 199,125 head in 1972, an average annual rate of increase of about 6%.[12] On the basis of 164 kilograms of boneless beef per animal slaughtered, meat production increased from about 20,400 metric tons in 1964 to 32,682 tons in 1972, with an estimated 7% of the cattle slaughtered in 1972 exported.

In 1970, three abattoirs (one at David and two near Panama City) processed approximately one-half of the total cattle slaughtered; the

11. J. Phillip Rourke, Livestock Marketing and Policy Considerations, GOP report, February 1973.
12. Based on preliminary data for 1972.

other half were processed at some 60 small, municipal abattoirs. The three major abattoirs supplied most of the dressed beef sold in the Panama City area. A large proportion of the cattle slaughtered in the two major abattoirs near Panama City are transported by truck for 200 kilometers or more from the central provinces of Cocle, Herrera, Los Santos, and Veraguas. Cattle from Chiriqui province usually are slaughtered at David and shipped chilled by truck to Panama City, a distance of approximately 480 kilometers.

Chilled beef accounts for an estimated 30% of retail beef sales in Panama City, a percentage expected to double by 1980.[13] The high percentage for chilled beef reflects the relatively high average per capita income in Panama City. A large proportion of total meat sales are handled by supermarkets with adequate cooling facilities, and many households have refrigerators. Unchilled beef is sold mostly in public markets. Ministry of Health regulations require that unchilled beef either be sold or discarded the same day received.

Most of the dressed beef distributed in municipalities and villages in the interior is handled and distributed unchilled, mainly through public markets. However, the number of supermarkets is increasing in the larger municipalities and urban centers of the interior. Many of these supermarkets have chilled meat cases for handling imported specialty meat products and are likely to handle increased amounts of chilled domestic beef in the future. The transition from unchilled to chilled beef will take place more slowly in the interior than it has in Panama City. The municipal abattoirs generally do not handle chilled beef, and the capacity of the three major abattoirs is barely adequate to supply the existing demand for chilled beef in David and Panama City. A new abattoir was scheduled to be in operation in David by 1973. Divisa has been suggested as an ideal location for another modern abattoir with a capacity of 25 to 40 head per hour.[14] Most of the municipal abattoirs are in need of extensive modernization, but few of them handle enough cattle to justify the investment necessary for processing high-quality beef under sanitary conditions. The small scale of operations of the municipal abattoirs also results in a loss of by-products such as tankage and bone meal. As the road system in the interior improves, the small municipal abattoirs will gradually be replaced by larger regional units. This transition will allow more complete utilization of by-products and improvements in the level of sanitation and will facilitate the switch to chilled beef and the introduction of beef grades.

Most exported beef is shipped boned and frozen. The shift from exporting live cattle to exporting frozen beef occurred rapidly in the

13. Donald B. Agnew, Economic Feasibility Study for Additional Cattle Slaughter Facilities in the Republic of Panama, USDA, Washington, D.C., February 1972.
14. Agnew, 1972.

mid-1960s. Only 2 head of live cattle were exported in 1968, compared to 7,337 head in 1962. Exports of fresh chilled and frozen beef, on the other hand, increased from 155 metric tons in 1962 to over 1,796 tons in 1960.

Panama appears to have enough slaughtering capacity to handle the number of livestock marketed during peak periods; however, approximately half of the existing capacity needs to be replaced by larger, modern facilities. Three new abattoirs, each with capacity for processing 30,000 to 50,000 head of cattle annually, should be adequate to handle expected increases in cattle marketings during the 1970s and would allow the closing of many of the municipal abattoirs. Part of the additional capacity could be provided by increasing the capacity of existing abattoirs. The total investment cost of three new facilities, each capable of processing 40,000 head annually, is estimated to be approximately B/2 million. This cost estimate does not include the cost of refrigerated trucks or operating capital requirements. The projections of beef exports presented in Chapter 4 suggest that very little additional capacity will be needed for handling frozen beef exports during this decade.

Most livestock marketed in Panama are sold strictly on a weight basis. There is some variation in farm prices between cows, steers, oxen, and bulls, but seldom any due to differences in the grade or quality of cattle within a given class. Meat sold in public markets is also sold by weight with little or no differences in price for different cuts or qualities. The supermarkets in the Panama City area gradually are introducing changes in the traditional pricing system for meat.

The introduction of grades and the standardization of cutting methods would facilitate differential pricing of beef and could benefit producers as well as consumers. Introduction of standardized cutting methods should not be difficult to accomplish since it primarily involves training meat cutters. The development of livestock grades appropriate for Panama is the more difficult task because consumers cannot identify differences in grades as easily as they can recognize differences in meat cuts. Very few cattle are grain fed, with the result that few cattle would grade choice by U.S. standards. National law prohibits slaughter of beef less than 340 kilograms liveweight; the percentage of mature animals marketed is therefore relatively high. The national consumer preference for grass-fed, lean beef must be taken into account by the grading system.

Preliminary study indicates that three grades for carcass beef would adequately cover most of the beef marketed. The top grade would include the better finished, younger animals. The middle grade would cover the major working grade and would encompass most of the best meat now produced. The bottom grade would be used primarily for industrial meats to be processed as ground beef or as canned meat products. Grades for live cattle can be developed more easily after the grading system for carcass beef is established.[15]

The quality of most of the beef marketed can be controlled by supervising the activities of only five or six abattoirs. The abattoirs are the point in the livestock marketing channel where prices are most easily regulated and sanitation of the marketing system can be influenced most readily. Efforts to improve the meat marketing system are likely to be most successful if they are concentrated on the abattoirs. The grading of beef carcasses at the abattoirs would allow the gradual introduction of differential pricing at both the farm and retail level. These changes should enhance the government's ability to ensure consumers the quality of beef they want at fair prices and also allow it to influence the type of beef produced and the location of beef production.

CONSUMER SHOPPING PATTERNS

Shopping patterns of 400 families in Panama City were studied in June 1971.[16] The sample was stratified on the basis of family income. Approximately 68% of the families surveyed had an income of less than B/300 monthly. Families with lower incomes were larger on the average than those with higher incomes. The average family with income less than B/25 monthly contained 7.36 persons, compared to 4.15 persons per family in the group with more than B/120 monthly.

In general, families with higher incomes purchased more of their food from supermarkets than families with lower incomes. Families in the lower income groups purchased the majority of their food at small, neighborhood stores, which usually would allow food purchases on credit. Nevertheless, supermarkets tended to be an important source for purchases of rice, milk, and canned foods, even for families in the lowest income group.

Ambulant salesmen were not an important source of food purchases for any of the income groups. Only 8% of the families in the lowest income group (income less than B/25 monthly) regularly purchased fruits and vegetables from ambulant salesmen, and none of the families in the highest income group (income greater than B/120 monthly) considered ambulant salesmen to be a regular source of any type of food item.

Central public markets did not appear to play as important a role in food marketing in Panama City as in other major cities in Latin America. Consumers who shopped regularly at central public markets apparently felt that these markets were a better source of meats, fruits,

15. Arnold A. Menchaca, Development of Grades and Standards for Carcass Beef for Panama, USDA, Panama, April 1972.
16. Nancy Fong, Estudio de Los Patrones de Consumo de Alimentos en la Ciudad de Panamá, SSC, Panama, March 1972.

and vegetables than of rice, milk, or canned goods. Despite these attitudes, only 18% of the families in the lowest income group regularly purchased meat at the central public market, and only 12% of the families in the highest income group did so. In the case of fruits and vegetables, 22% of the families in both the highest and the lowest income groups frequently made their purchases at the central public market. Shopping at the central public market generally was considered to be time consuming and inconvenient.

Shopping patterns revealed in the survey appear consistent with certain hypotheses. Supermarkets usually sell canned goods at lower prices than the public markets. Supermarkets and neighborhood stores with adequate cooling facilities usually are able to maintain the quality of milk and other perishable dairy products for longer periods and thus are considered the best places to buy these products. Central public markets are competitive with supermarkets in the price and quality of fruits and vegetables. High-income consumers usually prefer the chilled meat available at supermarkets rather than the unchilled meat available elsewhere. On the other hand, low-income consumers prefer unchilled meat but prefer to purchase it at neighborhood meat markets and food stores rather than the central public market because of convenience and availability of credit.

The study suggests that the relative importance of supermarkets in Panama City will continue to increase as real per capita income increases. Consumers generally considered supermarkets to be the best place to shop, except that they did not provide credit and usually were not as conveniently located as the neighborhood stores. Increases in per capita income will change shopping patterns by reducing the consumer's need to purchase food on credit as well as diminishing the relative importance of store location. The central public market's relative importance is likely to decline primarily because it is becoming increasingly difficult to reach as Panama City grows and traffic congestion in the downtown area increases.

FRUIT AND VEGETABLE MARKETING

The marketing systems for fresh fruits and vegetables are basically the same. Producers may sell their products in one of the following ways: (1) directly to wholesalers, who in turn supply the supermarket chains in Panama City; (2) to a government-operated collection center, which in turn may hold the product in cold storage for several weeks before delivery to wholesalers or retailers; (3) to a cooperative if the products are to be processed by one of the three major canning plants; or (4) to truck drivers who are wholesalers or represent wholesalers in the principal urban centers. These channels are basically the same in each of the three principal production areas which, ranked in the order of their relative importance, are (1) the upland areas of Chiriqui province; (2) the area near El Valle, including part of Panama province; and (3) the central provinces of Herrera, Los Santos, and Cocle.[17] As indicated in Chapter 4, Chiriqui province is the principal production center for potatoes, lettuce, cabbage, carrots, and beets.

Farmers consider the large variation in farm prices of most products and the lack of a secure market to be their principal marketing problems. The variations in prices are due partly to seasonality of production, partly to lack of outlook information, and partly to lack of market news on current farm and retail prices in the principal markets. Efforts are under way to improve the market news system, lengthen production seasons of some products, promote processing of more vegetables, and place more vegetables in cold storage during peak production periods. Programs in these areas will not provide short-term solutions to farmers' problems, but they do offer the best possibilities for reducing variations in farm prices in the long run.

From the wholesaler's viewpoint, the principal problems appear to be high costs of dealing with large numbers of small producers and lack of high-quality produce. It is likely that producers of most vegetables will continue to operate on a small scale at least until 1980. Large-scale operations would be extremely risky for producers operating with their own capital and producing for a relatively small, domestic market. Export possibilities .for most vegetables are limited. Production may tend to become more localized, and small producers may find it to their advantage to form marketing cooperatives, but neither of these events is likely to reduce wholesaler costs substantially. Although little reliable data are available, there is widespread agreement that marketing losses both in quantity and quality are high and could be reduced by the introduction of improved handling procedures and some additional investment in modern marketing facilities. Extension programs designed to promote the use of improved varieties and to illustrate the importance of proper harvesting, handling, and transportation of fruits and vegetables would help to improve the average quality of produce reaching consumers. Government price policies can have a significant impact on the willingness of wholesalers to invest in marketing facilities. If the prices set in public markets do not make adequate allowance for differences in qualities, there is little incentive to invest in packing sheds and sorting equipment. If retail prices are held constant throughout the year, there is less incentive to invest in storage facilities.

The major marketing problem of small retailers of fruits and vegetables in Panama City appears to be the large amount of time required to obtain produce daily. It is estimated that 99% of the fruits and vegetables purchased by small retailers are from wholesalers located in

17. Nancy J. Fong. Mercadeo de Frutas y Vegetales en Panamá. SSC. Panama. October 1971.

streets around the central market near the waterfront in downtown Panama City. Most small retailers go to the central market daily to make
their own purchases, a process that requires a minimum of one to two
hours daily. The existing central market is not only difficult to reach
but also lacks parking space and room for trucks to unload produce.
The construction of a new wholesale market in a more central location
would help to reduce the amount of time that retailers spend in purchasing their produce as well as to allow the introduction of improved handling procedures that would help raise the quality of the produce.

Supermarkets avoid some of the problems of small retailers by rely-
ing on wholesalers to deliver specified amounts of fruits and vegetables.
The supermarket chains in Panama City consign their produce department to one of the two major wholesalers. These wholesalers are responsible for selecting the fruits and vegetables, delivering them to the
stores, and displaying them for sale.

Very little information exists on marketing margins. The limited
data available indicate that the first wholesaler operates on a markup
of 10% to 20% above the price paid to farmers, and the second wholesaler probably operates on margins at least as large as those of the first.
Small retailers reportedly sell at average prices about 40% above the
final wholesale price.

Consumers see the end result of various marketing problems (high
prices, poor quality, and seasonal scarcities). The government could
reduce prices, improve the average quality, and eliminate seasonal
scarcities of some products by allowing increased importation of fruits
and vegetables. Although increased imports would benefit consumers
in the short run, they would not solve any of the basic marketing problems, would be detrimental to farmers, and probably would not benefit
consumers in the long run.

SUMMARY AND CONCLUSIONS

By Latin American standards, Panama's food marketing system is
above average. A large proportion of the basic foods marketed are
processed by companies with fairly modern, capital-intensive facilities,
supermarkets account for a relatively high proportion of total food sales,
and retail food prices during 1960–72 have been remarkably stable.

The capital-intensive nature of many food marketing channels
results from several factors. First, compared to many Latin American
countries, interest rates in Panama have been relatively low and wage
rates relatively high. Second, the scarcity of labor in some areas at certain times of the year has encouraged the use of capital-intensive technology. Large rice producers, for example, have found labor to be in
short supply during planting and harvesting seasons and have overcome
this difficulty through use of modern farm machinery. The bulk han-

dling of rice on large farms has complemented bulk storage and handling of grain by rice dealers. A third factor has been the dualistic nature of the agricultural sector. Large producers market most of their production and either become large wholesale and processing operations or create them. A few relatively large dairy farmers, for example, specialize in the production of Grade A milk, and most of their output is sold to one milk processor. The milk processing company in turn is able to operate on a large enough scale to justify investment in stainless steel tank trucks, cooling stations, and modern pasteurization equipment. Marketing channels reaching small farmers usually are less capital intensive than those reaching large farmers. Small farmers are more likely to sell their cattle to municipal abattoirs. The marketing system for fresh vegetables has not generated very much investment in packing sheds or cold storage facilities. Small milk producers are more likely to sell their milk to local dealers who distribute unpasteurized milk.

A fourth factor affecting the capital intensity of marketing channels has been the growth of supermarkets in Panama City. This growth is a reflection of the relatively high and increasing average income levels in the Panama City and Colon areas. Supermarkets buy on a large scale and prefer to deal with wholesalers who can consistently supply large quantities of high-quality products. Wholesalers have had to invest in larger storage facilities to assure consistent supplies and in the future may have to purchase additional processing and handling equipment in order to improve product quality. As a result, a capital-intensive retail system (supermarkets) tends to create a more capital-intensive wholesale system.

Most of the marketing channels for the major food products are controlled at some point by a small number of firms. The oligopolistic structure of the marketing channels cannot be altered to any great extent without reducing the operational efficiency of the markets. Existing firms are large relative to the national market, but most are still too small to take full advantage of economies of larger scale operations. The general trend appears to be toward even fewer and larger firms controlling marketing of most food items. Regional abattoirs gradually will replace small, municipal facilities. Supermarkets will continue to capture a larger share of urban food sales. It also seems likely that there will be an increased amount of vertical and horizontal integration in the food marketing industry. Several of the poultry marketing firms already are completely integrated from farm to final consumer, milk processing companies gradually are moving into vegetable processing, and the ability of supermarkets to undertake their own wholesale operations will increase as they become larger.

The oligopolistic nature of food marketing channels should make it easier for the government to control prices and to regulate food quality. Regulatory agencies must deal directly with only a few firms to alter market conduct and performance. While the government may not wish to alter the market structure of the main food marketing channels, it could give greater support to the development of farmer cooperatives in order to increase the market power of small and medium producers. It seems unlikely that there will be any less need for government price controls in the future than in the past, but there will be an increased need to allow seasonal price variations and greater differences in the prices of different qualities of food products. In the past, the government has tended to prevent the price system from providing farmers with information on the type and quantities of food products that consumers want. The prices set may have been fair and equitable when they were established, but they were not adjusted rapidly enough to signal changes in demand, a situation that reflects the importance assigned to price stability. A more sophisticated and flexible approach to price controls will be needed in the future.

CHAPTER SIX

PUBLIC SECTOR PROGRAMS FOR AGRICULTURAL DEVELOPMENT

UNTIL 1959, Panama's economic growth was achieved without much direct government involvement. Public sector efforts to foster economic development consisted mainly of tax and tariff exemptions granted to encourage private investment, road building, and construction of health and educational facilities. Monetary stability and favorable fiscal policies created an environment conducive to expansion of private economic activity in construction, industry, finance, and commerce.

Since 1960, and especially since 1968, government efforts supporting economic and social development have increased as a result of growing awareness of national needs and greater determination to promote economic equity and justice. To realize its development objectives, the Government of Panama has strengthened its planning activities, expanded its investment activities, and reorganized its institutions to support public and private development efforts.

THE PUBLIC SECTOR

The public sector consists of the national government, the autonomous institutions, the social security agency, and the municipalities. A brief review of overall government expenditures is given here as background for an analysis of several specific agricultural programs later in the chapter.

Current expenditures by the government have increased as its expanded development program has been implemented. Total current expenditures were B/159.5 million in 1971, compared with B/96.6 mil-

TABLE 6.1. • CURRENT EXPENDITURES BY FUNCTION

Function	Expenditures					Annual Growth Rate 1966-70	Revised Budget 1971
	1966	1967	1968	1969	1970		
	(millions of balboas)						
Administration	24.8	29.1	32.2	36.7	43.3	15.1%	46.7
Education	27.4	30.8	35.7	36.8	43.1	12.0%	42.2
Public Works	9.4	10.5	11.1	9.2	11.9	6.0%	10.5
Agriculture	4.0	4.8	5.2	5.7	6.0	20.1%[a]	6.5
Commerce and Industry				0.5	2.3		2.3
Health	14.8	17.7	18.3	17.6	19.4	9.4%[b]	21.5
Labor and Welfare				1.6	1.8		2.0
Subtotal	80.5	93.0	102.6	108.4	127.9	12.3%	131.7
Total Current Expenditures	96.6	106.8	117.0	129.6	159.5	13.7%	164.1

Source: Dirección de Estadística y Censo.

[a] Agriculture and commerce and industry are combined for the 1966-68 period. The annual growth rate is based on the combined budgets.

[b] Annual growth rate is based on the combined budgets of health and labor and welfare.

lion in 1966. Expenditures by major functional areas are shown in Table 6.1. These data reflect the operating budgets of the various ministries. Transfers to autonomous agencies and interest on the public debt account for the remainder. No separate Ministry of Agriculture existed until 1969. Since 1969, budget allocations for agriculture have represented 4% to 6% of current budget expenditures.

Revenues were B/181 million in 1971 and have increased at a rate well in excess of the average overall economic growth. Revenue increases since 1970 have resulted from new tax measures. Both personal and corporate income taxes have been increased, import taxes have been raised, and sales and excise taxes adjusted. In 1971, direct taxes, including taxes on income and property, totaled B/69.6 million. Indirect taxes, including taxes on foreign trade and sales and excise taxes, totaled B/73.8 million. Nontax revenues accounted for the remaining B/37.7 million in government revenues.

Total government investment expenditures rose substantially between 1960 and 1970. An analysis of public investment is presented in Table 6.2. Investment in road construction and maintenance accounted for 37% of total public sector investment in 1970. Public investment in agriculture doubled between 1969 and 1970. Further increases in public investment in this sector will be necessary to finance an overall sector development program. Major public sector investment projects now under way include the B/100 million Darien Gap highway project financed in large part by a $60 million grant from the United States, a rural road development project financed by an Inter-American Development Bank (IDB) loan, and construction of airport and tourism facilities.

The government is striving to organize a coordinated investment program to meet Panama's development needs. The 1971–75 program will emphasize economic infrastructure as well as directly productive investments. Considerable investments are anticipated in education as well as in rural health, water supply, and housing. The Bayano Dam project near Panama City is under way, and a major Colon-Panama highway project is scheduled. Directly productive investments include an agricultural sector program, port and fisheries facilities, cattle, and tourism. The size of the planned program will create heavy demand for internal public savings as well as external financing.

MINISTRY OF AGRICULTURAL DEVELOPMENT

The need for greater control and coordination of Panama's agricultural development programs was recognized officially with the formation of the Ministry of Agricultural Development (MIDA) in January 1973. The reorganization made MIDA responsible for a much wider range of agricultural development programs than existed under the

TABLE 6.2. ● PUBLIC SECTOR INVESTMENT, 1969–75

Sector	Actual 1969	Actual 1970	Budgeted 1971	Budgeted 1972	IBRD Projections 1973	IBRD Projections 1974	IBRD Projections 1975
	(millions of balboas)						
Agriculture	3.55 (1.54)[a]	7.15 (3.84)	7.65 (4.65)	12.86 (6.88)	13.54 (9.55)	8.45 (5.80)	7.55 (4.95)
Commerce and Industry	1.31 (0.51)	0.78 (--)	9.83 (--)	8.45 (0.40)	3.40 (2.70)	7.60 (4.90)	8.70 (6.00)
Electrification	2.45 (0.06)	7.90 (1.20)	7.56 (3.14)	12.36 (8.32)	15.48 (10.64)	15.00 (10.90)	17.00 (12.20)
Education	3.88 (0.35)	4.83 (0.61)	9.69 (4.18)	10.96 (6.83)	8.27 (4.03)	5.09 (2.86)	8.90 (4.40)
Health and Water	9.97 (6.24)	8.61 (5.38)	21.31 (6.40)	11.54 (8.40)	14.20 (10.41)	17.41 (9.83)	18.50 (10.60)
Housing	6.90 (3.68)	11.03 (5.51)	11.11 (6.00)	1.50 (1.50)	7.00 (5.00)	8.70 (6.20)	3.20 (2.00)
Multisector	-- (--)	0.31 (0.08)	1.40 (1.09)	0.28 (0.18)	1.25 (0.88)	0.88 (0.60)	-- (--)
Tourism	-- (--)	2.07 (--)	0.80 (--)	0.55 (0.30)	2.05 (1.30)	5.55 (3.00)	4.05 (2.00)
Roads	23.78 (3.55)	27.49 (4.00)	10.67 (3.27)	26.55 (19.05)	43.05 (31.89)	44.16 (33.02)	33.37 (27.63)
Public Buildings	9.92 (--)	3.03 (--)	0.45 (--)	-- (--)	-- (--)	-- (--)	-- (--)
Total	61.76 (15.94)	73.20 (20.59)	80.48 (28.68)	85.08 (51.86)	108.24 (76.79)	112.84 (77.11)	105.27 (69.78)

Source: Panamanian Planning Office and IBRD mission estimates.

[a]Figures in brackets are external loans or grants from AID, IBRD, IDB, NNDP, OAS, and EXIM Bank.

Ministry of Agriculture and Livestock (MAG). Prior to the creation of MIDA, numerous government agencies were carrying out programs serving the agricultural sector. A review of Panama's administrative structure in 1970 identified 14 different institutions providing services to agriculture.

The newly formed MIDA has central authority and responsibility for public programs involving production, marketing, social development and farmer organizations, agrarian reform, plant and livestock sanitation, renewable agricultural resources, sector planning, and overall agricultural development policy. The personnel and functions of the Agrarian Reform Commission (CRA) were assigned to the new ministry. Marketing functions and personnel from the Institute of Economic Development (IFE) were shifted to MIDA. The credit programs for small and medium farmers, formerly administered by IFE and MAG, were transferred to the new Agricultural Development Bank. The ministry is to provide policy direction for agricultural credit programs while the Agricultural Development Bank is to maintain financial control of the lending activities.

Operational activities of MIDA are assigned to three national directorates, eight general directorates, and eight regional directorates. The national directorates are responsible for production, marketing, and agrarian reform programs. The general directorates are to carry out activities in the areas of (1) social development, (2) engineering, (3) development projects, (4) administrative affairs, (5) sector planning, (6) renewable natural resources, (7) agricultural industries, and (8) secondary agricultural education. The regional directorates are organized primarily on a provincial basis.

Among the specific functions assigned to MIDA are the following:

1. Modify agricultural structures that impede the improvement of living conditions of the rural population and establish mechanisms that will permanently guarantee a rational and equitable use of the land and renewable natural resources.
2. Take measures to guarantee agricultural producers (especially small and medium producers) just prices for their products, taking into account the interests of domestic consumers.
3. Organize and assist the campesino population in order to promote better utilization of the nation's land and renewable resources.
4. Stimulate, create, and operate directly, or in association with public or private business, national or international processing activities for agricultural products.
5. Realize directly, or in collaboration with other government agencies and communities, the works that will support the development of agricultural production.

6. Determine and direct credit and finance policy for the agricultural sector, giving emphasis and priority to the needs of marginal farmers and fishermen and to small and medium farmers.
7. Assist other agencies to ensure that rural workers can procure employment and adequate remuneration along with medical and social security benefits.
8. Regulate and adopt sanitary control measures for agricultural products.
9. Formulate and execute agricultural development plans.
10. Promote, operate, and coordinate research programs, experiment stations, demonstration fields, institutions, and centers or schools for the training of farmers, campesinos, and government officials.
11. Produce, distribute, certify, regulate, import, process, rent, sell, and donate equipment, machinery, and other inputs, and in general, undertake all types of programs necessary to stimulate and expand the utilization of better inputs and technical improvements in agricultural production.
12. Collaborate with the Office of Price Control to determine prices of inputs, agricultural machinery, and equipment.
13. Apply and carry out the Agrarian Code and its legal annexes.
14. Regulate, inspect, and control the introduction of meat and livestock into the country, the slaughter of livestock for consumption, and the breeding and fattening of beef and dairy cattle.
15. Establish support prices for domestic agricultural products.
16. Import, free of taxes, those agricultural products necessary for programs developed by MIDA or for human consumption when local production is not enough to supply local demand.
17. Export, free of taxes, surplus agricultural production when this would be in the best interests of the country.
18. Install and operate (directly or in association with private business, communities, and municipalities) enterprises for the receipt, processing, packaging, conservation, storage, transportation, distribution, and sale of agricultural products.
19. Authorize guarantees for agricultural or agricultural-industrial activities to individual small producers or to their associations.
20. Any other functions assigned by the law or regulations.

This is not a complete list of the responsibilities of MIDA, but it is adequate to illustrate the broad range of activities under ministry control. It is readily apparent that MIDA's actions will have a substantial impact on nearly all aspects of Panama's future agricultural development.

AGRARIAN REFORM

In 1964, the Agrarian Reform Commission began a rural cadastre in collaboration with other government agencies. The cadastre was planned to cover 53% of the national territory where 95% of the population lives in order to provide a basis for agrarian policy and land taxation. The goal was to identify the ownership of every plot, use of the land, soil type and physical characteristics, value, and potential use. The collection of data for the cadastre was essentially finished by 1973 but had not yet been completely codified and summarized.

In 1966, the commission's goal was to aid 70,000 families on small farms without title or without land and with incomes of less than B/200 per year. The most optimistic assessment of the program would show that by 1973 not more than a fourth of this number of families had been benefited. Moreover, many of those aided through grants of land or title remain poor due to lack of credit, technical assistance, and infrastructure. Beginning in 1969, the commission initiated a program to acquire lands and organize cooperative farms called asentamientos. By the end of 1971, 109 asentamientos involving 5,200 families had been organized. During January-March 1972, an additional 27 asentamientos containing 825 families were constituted.[1] Since 1969, the asentamientos have received priority for credit, technical assistance, and production inputs available to the commission.

In 1971–72, the asentamientos used 5,000 hectares of land for production on a communal basis. Members of the asentamientos may also hold private parcels not included in the area farmed collectively. Also, some have little land and concentrate on intensive production of poultry and hogs. Rice, corn, and beans accounted for 99% of the collective production. Plans have been made to diversify production by devoting up to 10% of the land in asentamientos to vegetables, bananas, and other fruits.

Members of the asentamientos earn income from collective production, from production on private plots, and from salaries for work done on large farms. Expectations for 1972–73 were that production on the asentamientos would result in an average income per family of about B/220, varying from B/300 or more per family in Chiriqui, to B/150 in Veraguas, to less than B/100 in Colon. No data are available on income earned from other sources by members of the asentamientos.

The three major action alternatives available within the agrarian reform program are (1) granting of land titles, (2) redistribution of idle lands held by large farmers, and (3) formation of asentamientos or individual farms for small farmers and landless laborers. None of these

---

1. Comisión de Reforma Agraria, Memoria, 1972.

actions will do much to improve labor productivity and income distribution in the agricultural sector unless they form part of an integrated approach to the formation of viable production units (collective or individual) that have access to credit and technical assistance.

AGRICULTURAL CREDIT

Prior to the formation of the Agricultural Development Bank in January 1973, the four main sources of agricultural credit were (1) private banks, (2) private merchants, (3) the National Bank of Panama, and (4) IFE. These credit sources have different clientele and lend money on different terms, but each has played an important role in helping farmers increase their productivity.

Private banks are the most important source of institutional credit in terms of total amount of money. At least seven private banks with branch offices are outside Panama City and provide credit directly to farmers and agricultural businesses. Many of the other private banks provide some agricultural credit indirectly by financing imports of agricultural inputs and equipment or by lending to exporters of agricultural products.

The Chase Manhattan Bank was the first major bank to actively promote agricultural credit. Chase Manhattan's successful experience in livestock financing during the 1950s led other private banks to establish agricultural credit departments staffed with specialists in agriculture, livestock, and agribusiness management.

Private banks direct most of their agricultural credit to large-scale farmers, agribusinesses, sugar manufacturers, and banana producers. Credit to the agricultural sector is subject to the same controls applied to loans for other activities. Borrowers must be able to present adequate guarantees and usually must be well established in their agricultural businesses. About 60% of the portfolios of private banks are guaranteed with land mortgages. Interest rates in 1973 averaged between 9% and 10.5% for short-term loans secured by personal signature of chattel mortgages and 11% for long-term (five-year) loans secured by land or buildings.

Private merchants use credit primarily as a means of increasing their sales of inputs such as machinery and fertilizer or ensuring the availability of farm products such as rice and coffee. The tobacco industry finances producers under contract and provides technical assistance. Sugar manufacturers provide fertilizer and seed on credit to producers. The volume of credit from these sources is unknown. Part of the credit from private merchants represents a relending of money that the merchants borrow from private banks. Private merchants usually charge higher interest rates than private banks and most loans are for a short term only, although they usually can be obtained more quickly and with less paper work than from either private banks or public lending agencies.

The National Bank of Panama operates under lending policies similar to private banks. Interest rates range from 8% to 9%, plus a 1% inspection fee. Personal signatures and chattel mortgages are accepted as guarantees for loans to hog and poultry producers, but most loans for cattle are guaranteed by livestock or land. Most of the National Bank's agricultural credit portfolio consists of loans to medium and large farmers. During 1970, the bank made 207 loans for "agriculture" and 1,717 loans for "livestock," primarily cattle. Nearly 68% of the bank's total loans were for amounts between B/1,500 to B/2,499. The total amount loaned for "agriculture" was B/1,040,000 and for "livestock," B/5.3 million. Approximately half of the bank's agricultural credit funds are obtained from IDB loans which emphasize medium and large cattle, hog, and poultry operations.

Until 1973, IFE provided agricultural credit with funds obtained from IDB and AID loans to MAG. The AID loans to MAG were intended primarily for small farmers while IDB loans to IFE were directed primarily to medium farmers.

During 1970, nearly 39% of the B/6.6 million loaned by IFE was for crops.[2] Over 50% of these funds went to rice producers. About 75% of the crop loans were short-term loans for operating capital. Over 95% of the livestock credit went to cattle producers. Approximately 90% of the livestock loans was for medium-term capital investments.

The majority of the 1970 IFE loans were secured by chattel mortgages on crops, livestock, or equipment. Land was used for security for less than 3% of the loans. Interest rates ranged from 4% to 8%, depending on the source of funds; IFE also charged a 1% inspection fee.

The MAG cooperated with IFE by assigning extension agents to provide technical assistance to small farmers receiving loans from IFE. The MAG agents made the first contact with farmers, obtained credit information, and made initial recommendations. If IFE approved the loan, purchase orders were issued by MAG for the services and materials to be financed, and IFE made disbursements as invoices were presented. The MAG credit agents remained responsible for supervision and collection of the account.

The amount of agricultural credit available from private banks, IFE, and the National Bank (institutional sources) increased from B/6,020,000 in 1960 to B/29,480,000 in 1970, nearly a 400% increase in credit availability over the 11-year period (Table 6.3). The largest increases in credit availability occurred between 1963–64, 1966–67, and 1969–70 (measured in terms of 1960 balboas). Private banks supplied about 60% of agricultural credit during the 1960s. The agricultural

2. Charles P. Swett, Agricultural Credit Situation, final report, GOP report, December 1971.

TABLE 6.3. • AGRICULTURAL CREDIT BY AGENCY, 1960–70

Year	Private Banks[a]	Banco Nacional	IFE	Total
	(millions of 1960 balboas)			
1960	3.76	1.70	0.56	6.02
1961	5.53	1.28	0.73	7.54
1962	5.19	3.06	0.95	9.20
1963	5.82	2.78	1.01	9.61
1964	8.28	2.86	2.44	13.58
1965	7.29	3.76	2.11	13.16
1966	5.71	3.15	2.55	11.41
1967	10.31	4.19	2.77	17.27
1968	9.82	5.38	3.20	18.40
1969	14.34	5.06	4.04	23.44
1970	17.70	5.18	6.60	29.48
Total Percent Increase	370	204	1,078	390
Average Annual Percent Increase	34	19	98	35
Compound Annual Percent Increase	15	10	25	15

Source: Swett, 1971.

[a]Private bank credit does not include credit to sugar manufacturers.

credit available from the National Bank increased by about 200% between 1960 and 1970, but its relative importance as a source of credit declined. In 1970, the National Bank supplied only 17% of the institutional credit compared to about 28% in 1960. On the other hand, IFE supplied only 9% of the institutional credit for agriculture in 1960 and over 22% in 1970.

The percentage of total domestic credit going to agriculture increased only slightly during the 1965–70 period (Table 6.4). Agricultural

TABLE 6.4. • DISTRIBUTION OF AGRICULTURAL CREDIT TO CROPS AND LIVESTOCK, 1965–70

Year	Agricultural Loans as % of Total Domestic Loans	Livestock Loans as % of Total Agricultural Loans	Crop Loans as % of Total Agricultural Loans
	(%)	(%)	(%)
1965	6.1	61.8	38.2
1966	6.5	72.3	27.7
1967	7.9	54.8	45.2
1968	8.3	63.3	36.7
1969	7.4	63.3	36.7
1970	8.6	60.0	40.0

Source: Swett, 1971.

credit from institutional sources accounted for approximately 8.6% of total domestic credit in 1970. About two-thirds of the agricultural credit from institutional sources during the 1960s went to livestock, primarily cattle. The rapid growth of agricultural credit from IFE reflects the efforts of the Government of Panama and the international lending agencies to increase the percentage of total credit allocated for crop loans.

Credit Needs

Experience in the United States and elsewhere indicates that short-term credit requirements for agriculture range between 40% and 50% of the annual value of agricultural production. An additional amount equal to at least 50% of the value of annual production should be available for medium-term and long-term credit (for land improvements, buildings, equipment, breeding stock, etc.). If these percentages are used, the total amount of agricultural credit needed equals approximately the annual value of agricultural production.[3]

No reliable estimates of the total amount of agricultural credit are available from private merchants. If they supplied as much credit in 1970 as institutional sources and if the amount of credit needed was equal to the value of agricultural production, total agricultural credit

3. Paul A. Holden, Agricultural Credit in Panama, GOP report, June 1969.

available was at least B/50 million less than the amount needed. This rough estimate suggests that farmers are providing a large part of their credit needs from personal savings and probably do not have as much capital as they could utilize productively (estimate does not include amounts needed for forestry or fisheries).

The relative importance of institutions as credit sources appears to have increased substantially during the 1960s. Assuming that the amount of credit needed is equal to the value of production, institutional sources supplied about 8% of the credit needed in 1960 and 27% in 1970.

If a linear trend projection based on the 1960–70 data in Table 6.3 is used, institutional sources would provide about B/48 million of agricultural credit in 1980, roughly 30% of the total agricultural credit needed. If institutional credit could be increased at a 10% rate compounded annually beginning from the 1969 credit level, total agricultural credit from these sources would be approximately B/66.7 million by 1980, or roughly 43% of the total needed. The compounded rate of increase in institutional credit during the 1960s was approximately 15%. Actual credit available by 1980 probably will fall within the B/48 to B/66.7 million range, depending on the actions of the international lending agencies.

Additional medium-term and long-term credit will be needed by medium and large livestock operations as the Darien region is opened. The private banking system is expected to meet the needs for this type of credit. The greatest need during this period is for (1) medium-term and long-term development loans for medium farm operators who do not have the type of security presently required by private banks and (2) a source of production credit for small farm operators who have a strong requirement for technical assistance.

The government efforts to increase the amount of credit available to small and medium farmers have encountered numerous difficulties. Inadequate screening of credit applications resulted in the approval of loans to farmers living in areas that were difficult for extension agents to reach. The shortage of well-trained technicians to guide farmers in the use of improved technology prevented them from realizing the maximum benefits from credit. Lack of adequate transportation facilities reduced the effectiveness of the available extension agents. A 1972 survey (carried out in the provinces of Los Santos, Herrera, and Veraguas) of small-grain farmers receiving loans and technical assistance suggested that availability of technical assistance did very little to increase farm incomes unless that assistance resulted in increased use of fertilizer.[4]

The salary and support costs of keeping a supervised credit agent with a perito agropecuario degree in the field is at least B/6,000 annually. If the agent supervises 400 small loans of B/500 each, his total "portfolio" is B/200,000. The lending agency would have to earn at least 3%

---

4. J. Duque, Loans to Small Farmers, GOP report, Panama, 1972.

above its other costs to support a supervised credit agent with a portfolio of this size. Even with adequate transportation, it would be difficult for an agent to provide close technical assistance to 400 small farmers. Thus, even if all loans are collected, it seems likely that the lending agency would either lose money on its loans to small farmers or the farmers would not receive adequate technical assistance from the credit agents. These difficulties can be reduced somewhat by having credit agents "balance" their portfolios by adding some larger, medium, and long term loans to medium farmers. Such loans would require less supervision than short-term production loans to small farmers. In this way, a credit agent could be effectively utilized in cost terms and also provide technical assistance to small farmers.

TRAINING AGRICULTURAL TECHNICIANS

There were 816 agricultural technicians working in the public sector in 1972; approximately 290 were ingenieros agrónomos with university training. Another 471 had intermediate level training and were classified as bachilleres agropecuarios. The remaining 45 were peritos agropecuarios with vocational level training.

A study made by the Ministry of Agriculture in 1972 suggested that approximately 1,700 additional specialists in agricultural sciences would be needed by the public sector between 1973 and 1977 to carry out existing and proposed development programs.[5] The ministry study also indicated that the maximum number of agricultural technicians that would be graduated during the 1973–77 period was approximately 1,180, which seems an optimistic supply projection. Even if this projection were achieved, the demand would exceed the supply by about 500 technicians.

Only 15 ingenieros agrónomos graduated from the University of Panama during the 1971–72 school year. Approximately 100 bachilleres agropecuarios graduated from the main technical schools in 1971–72; the two most important schools are the National Agricultural Institute (INA) at Divisa and Felix Olivares at David.

The National Agricultural Institute

The INA is a three-year technical high school that emphasizes learning by doing.[6] It is the main source of middle level agricultural technicians for both the public and private sector; therefore, INA would play an important role in any program designed to increase agricultural productivity through the introduction of new technology.

5. Ing. Ruben González and Lic. Antonio Gordon, Adiestaramiento Técnico Bosquejo Preliminar, Ministry of Agriculture, Panama, July 1972.
6. This section is based on Kermit H. Adams, Preliminary Report on Instituto Nacional de Agricultura—Dr. Augusto Samuel Boyd, Divisa, Panama, March 1972. Adams was an advisor to the Director of the Instituto Técnico de Agricultura, Barcena, Guatemala, from 1967 to 1973.

The institute is located near the town of Divisa, about 215 kilometers from Panama City. It has approximately 725 hectares of land; about 110 hectares are used for field crops and 420 for pastures. The remaining 195 hectares are hilly and rocky. A good part of the area is inundated annually during the rainy season, which limits the amount of land available for some types of research projects.

Over 750 technicians have graduated from INA since it was founded in 1941. Total enrollment in 1971 was 285 students. During the five-year period from 1967 to 1971, the average graduating class contained 42 students. It is estimated that INA could now place 100 to 120 graduates annually. A student body of 450 to 500 students would be required to supply this demand.

Most graduates begin working in the public sector at salaries of B/175 to B/200 per month. The private sector pays about B/150 per month for newly graduated bachilleres agropecuarios, a situation that changes as the young graduate gains experience. A bachiller agropecuario with two years experience, for example, can expect a salary of about B/250 per month with a private company.

The teaching staff at INA in 1971 consisted of 30 regular professors and about 20 field assistants and research technicians. The institute has had a high rate of teacher turnover, due partly to salary levels and partly to personal considerations. Increased social and economic incentives will be necessary if INA is to enlarge and improve its teaching staff.

The enlargement of the training programs at INA would require substantial investments in equipment, new buildings, and land improvements. The estimated cost of the five-year program outlined by Adams was B/1,339,000. His program provided B/240,000 for faculty scholarships, B/869,000 for new buildings and equipment, and B/230,000 in technical assistance services. These cost estimates did not provide funds for land reclamation, irrigation, improved faculty housing, or better elementary school facilities. Including these items, the total cost of the five-year improvement program would be approximately B/1.5 million.

Expansion of INA programs would require an increase in the annual operating budget. With a total enrollment of 450 to 500 students plus short courses for 2,500 to 3,000 adults annually, the INA operating budget would have to be increased by approximately B/250,000 by the end of the five-year improvement program. Assuming that the operating budget was increased to this level gradually by adding an additional B/50,000 annually, the total increase in operating costs for the five-year period would be B/750,000.

There are no detailed studies of the value of education in Panama, and only rough estimates can be made of the benefits resulting from the expansion of INA programs. It is assumed that the improvement program outlined by Adams would provide the following results each year over a 20-year period:

1. Fifty additional bachilleres agropecuarios would be graduated annually.
2. One hundred additional students would be trained annually but would drop out before they graduated.
3. One thousand additional adults would participate in INA short courses annually.
4. Annual operating costs would be increased by B/250,000.
5. As a result of the training received at INA, a bachiller agropecuario would be able to increase his productivity by B/1,000 per year during a 20-year period after graduation.
6. Students who began the program at INA, but who did not graduate, would be able to increase their productivity by B/300 annually over a 20-year period as a result of the training received.
7. Each adult participating in a short course would be able to increase his productivity by B/100 per year for a five-year period after taking the course.
8. Increases in productivity and in operating expenses are discounted at a 10% interest rate over a 20-year period.

Under these assumptions, the discounted value of the expected increases in productivity is approximately B/9,675,000. The discounted value of the increased operating expenses over a 20-year period is B/2,128,500; added to this is the B/1.5 million investment cost of the expansion program. Dividing the B/9,675,000 in benefits by the total costs of B/3,628,500 results in a benefit-cost ratio of 2.7, based on the direct benefits to the participants in INA programs. The indirect benefits, resulting from the participants showing other farmers how to increase their productivity, should be at least equal to the direct benefits. The results certainly indicate that the expansion program is a worthwhile undertaking.

If all the investment costs and half the increased operating costs are allocated to the bachiller agropecuario program, the adult education program has a benefit-cost ratio of about 3.0. Two important advantages of the adult education program are that it reaches more people and the results are more readily identifiable by the participants.

Agricultural Education in the University of Panama

The agricultural program at the University of Panama is relatively new.[7] The School of Agriculture was established in 1959 as a part of the sciences program. It became a separate program in 1965 with the establishment of the College of Agriculture. In 1969, the agricultural

7. Much of this section is based on John W. Sites et al., Agricultural Research and Higher Education in Panama, Center for Tropical Agriculture, Institute of Food and Agricultural Sciences, University of Florida, Gainesville, September 1971.

education program was divided into two specializations; plant science and animal science. A program in home economics was added in 1971.

The main objectives of the College of Agriculture are to train agronomists and livestock specialists so that they may contribute to solving Panama's agricultural problems and to accelerate agricultural research. The college emphasizes science rather than applied agriculture. Vocational training in agriculture is left to schools such as INA.

In 1972, the College of Agriculture had approximately 20 full- and part-time professors and a support staff consisting of about 25 teaching and research assistants, secretaries, and helpers. Class and laboratory teaching contact time for each faculty member averaged about six hours per week. The balance of their time was devoted to research, including the supervision of thesis work of fifth-year students.

The field laboratory facilities are located near the International Airport at Tocumen, approximately ten miles from the university. Adequate research plots for the plant sciences laboratories are at this location. Research facilities for beef cattle are also available, but no facilities for swine, poultry, or dairy cattle. The soil and climate at Tocumen are not typical of many other areas of Panama; therefore, results of the research projects do not necessarily apply to other regions.

The ingeniero agrónomo is a five-year degree program. The first two years are largely devoted to general and basic sciences. A research program with thesis is required during the student's fifth year. The dropout rate is high with less than 25% of students who enter the program graduating.

The majority of students enrolling in the College of Agriculture are not from rural areas. Over 77% of students enrolled in 1967–68, for example, came from the province of Panama, primarily from Panama City. About 40% of graduates from the college are from the province of Panama, 20% are from Chiriqui province, and 15% from Cocle.

One source of rural students is the INA. Between 1959–70, 40% of Divisa graduates enrolled in the College of Agriculture. Only seven of the 90 Divisa students entering the program between 1959 and 1966 graduated, a dropout rate of over 90%.

Since there are no living facilities on campus, students from areas other than Panama City have housing problems and higher living costs. One method of attracting more rural students to the University of Panama would be special scholarships to offset these higher costs, which might help to reduce the dropout rate of rural students.

Graduates with the ingeniero agrónomo degree are in strong demand. The college estimates it could place at least 40 each year, but only about 15 students graduated annually during the 1967–72 period. Over 50% of the graduates are employed by government agencies, primarily MIDA. Based on present enrollments and past dropout rates, the College of Agriculture should graduate an average of 17 to 18 ingenieros agrónomos annually during the 1973–77 period. This is far short of the number that could be employed productively in Panama's agricultural development programs.

Several approaches could be used to increase the number of graduates. One would be to make the program easier, which could be accomplished by reducing the number of hours required for graduation, simplifying the more difficult courses, and providing additional assistance for students having difficulties or lacking adequate background for key courses. An alternative approach would be to increase scholarships or assistantships available to students needing financial aid. An easier program and increased financial assistance probably would not increase the total number of graduates during the 1973–77 period by more than about 20 to 25 students. The largest increases would not occur until 1976 and 1977.

Enlarged and improved facilities will be required if the college is to graduate more than 20 to 25 ingenieros agrónomos annually, and it seems unlikely that such facilities will be available prior to 1975. If enrollment could be doubled by 1975–76, graduating classes during the early 1980s would average 40 to 50 ingenieros agrónomos annually. Doubling enrollment would require doubling the existing faculty and staff.

The following assumptions are made in order to estimate the benefits and costs of enlarging the College of Agriculture's program:

1. Enrollment will be increased by 175 students, giving a total enrollment of approximately 350.
2. The college's annual operating budget will be increased by B/250,000 to provide for additional faculty and staff.
3. A B/1 million building program will be undertaken.
4. The annual cost of the building program, when amortized over a 20-year period using a 10% interest rate, is approximately B/120,000.
5. Fifty ingenieros agrónomos will be graduated annually within five years after the beginning of the expansion program.
6. Scholarships totaling B/50,000 annually will be provided for students from rural areas.
7. The annual salaries of persons trained in the College of Agriculture are increased by B/500 for each year they remain in the program.
8. The salary increases are discounted at 10% over a 20-year period and used as a measure of the benefits received from the enlarged training program.

Under these assumptions, the total annual benefits of the program are approximately B/745,000, and the total annual costs are B/420,000. The resulting benefit-cost ratio of 1.8 is lower than that of the program proposed for the INA.

Graduate Training in Foreign Universities

Very few Panamanians are receiving advanced training in agricultural sciences. Given the small size of the graduating classes of the College of Agriculture and the general shortage of agricultural specialists, it seems unlikely that more than about ten candidates could be identified annually for advanced training outside Panama. The costs and potential results of an eight-year graduate training program beginning in 1974 have been estimated, assuming that scholarships are provided for ten new graduate students annually for the first five years of the program. It is assumed that 35 students will obtain M.S. degrees, 10 will receive the Ph.D., and 5 will not complete their studies. The total cost of the training program, assuming B/7,000 per scholarship year, is estimated to be B/840,000. Graduates with M.S. degrees would begin to return to Panama in 1976, those with the Ph.D. would begin to complete their studies in 1978.

It is estimated that graduates with M.S. degrees should be able to earn at least B/4,000 more annually than an ingeniero agrónomo, while those with Ph.D. degrees are expected to earn B/8,000 more annually. It is assumed that the salary differences measure the value of the productivity increases resulting from the advanced training, a conservative assumption. The discounted value of the salary differences over a 20-year period, using a 10% discount rate, is approximately B/1,870,000. Dividing the total benefits by the estimated program costs results in a benefit-cost ratio of 2.2. Varying the size of the program in the range of 5 to 15 new scholarships annually probably would not alter the benefit-cost ratio significantly. A graduate training program of approximately this scale will be needed if agricultural teaching and research programs are to be expanded significantly.

AGRICULTURAL RESEARCH

Panama's main agricultural research programs are carried out by the College of Agriculture at the University of Panama and by MIDA. The research program at the University of Panama is loosely knit since individual faculty members for the most part determine the nature and character of their research programs. The research topics selected frequently depend on faculty member contact with government officials, former students, and farm operators. All projects are approved by the faculty research council, but there do not appear to be any criteria or general plan for determining the importance of various research programs or for assigning priorities to various projects. In general, members of the faculty of agronomy are well trained and highly competent; nearly all the professors hold the Ph.D. or M.S. degree from foreign universities.

The research program of MIDA is more highly organized than that of the College of Agriculture. Ministry research is almost entirely applied, with many of the research plots being used for demonstration purposes. Major emphasis has been placed on determining which plant varieties are best suited for Panama with special attention devoted to rice and, to a lesser extent, corn. Some work on vegetables has been carried out at the field station at Cerro Punta, while work on tomato breeding is being undertaken at Divisa. Other research projects include the rice program at Campo Llanos, Zone 4, the rice and corn program at Alanje, and the beef cattle program at Gualaca.

In 1971, a team of agricultural specialists from the University of Florida was requested "to evaluate the present agricultural research and higher agricultural education programs in Panama and make recommendations for a five-year program designed to accelerate the development of new farm level technology in Panama and to improve the related educational function of the University of Panama College of Agriculture."[8] They concluded that closer coordination would increase the effectiveness of agricultural research, teaching, and extension programs. The team suggested that this coordination could be achieved by establishing a research institute guided by an advisory council of persons from the College of Agriculture and various government agencies. It also was suggested that the research programs of the institute be organized on a commodity basis (grains, fruits, vegetables, livestock, etc.) to be coordinated closely with government extension programs. The national headquarters would be located at Tocumen and the main regional offices at Alanje in Chiriqui province and at Divisa.

The staff and facilities of the institute would be built up gradually over a five-year period. The total funding needed during the first five years was estimated to be B/671,200 for new buildings and equipment and B/3,946,423 for salaries and operating expenses of the professional and administrative staff. By the end of the five-year period, the institute would employ 116 persons.

If the research program outlined by the University of Florida team were carried out, total expenditures for salaries and operating expenses during the program's fifth year would be B/1,164,410. To this expenditure must be added an annual cost of roughly B/80,000 to amortize the proposed investments in new buildings and equipment over a 20-year period. A program of this size would have to increase the gross value of agricultural output by over B/2,489,000 annually to generate a benefit-cost ratio of 2.0.

Using a linear trend projection of the 1960 data, agricultural output in 1980, excluding bananas, forestry, and fishing, would be approximately B/155 million (gross value at 1960 prices). Assuming annual expendi-

8. Sites et al., 1971.

tures are held constant after the fifth year of the proposed program, the total expenditures on agricultural research would be approximately 0.8% of the value of agricultural output in 1980.

It is doubtful that a research program as large as that suggested by the University of Florida team could be implemented as rapidly as proposed originally. Even if a scholarship program for advanced training in agricultural sciences were initiated by 1974, the specialists needed for the proposed research program would not be available until the late 1970s.

MARKET NEWS

Market news is essential for the efficient operation of any marketing system. Reliable information on current supplies, prices, and demands is essential for effective decision making by producers, wholesalers, and retailers.

Prior to 1971, the only market news office in Panama was located in Panama City. This office reported wholesale prices paid by retailers for approximately 70 commodities which included meat, poultry, eggs, fish, fresh fruit, and vegetables. The office covered the Panama City Central Market and the smaller Calidonia Market. Average prices were released the following day.

Beginning in 1971, a system was developed by which prices and other market information were made available for dissemination the morning the data were collected. This information was wired immediately to growing areas and was broadcast daily by Panama's largest radio station, Radio MIA. Market news reporters were located in Capira, Penonome, Chitre, Santiago, David, Divisa, Cerro Punta, and Colon to provide the Panama City office with market information on such matters as prices, weather, and volume of produce.[9]

Considerable progress has been made in expanding and improving Panama's market news system since 1971. Further progress can be expected as personnel are trained, the radio phone system is enlarged, and vehicles are provided for market news reporters. Other government agencies are cooperating with the market news system in the development of grades and standards and in the expansion of the inspection station system for checking the movement of agricultural products.

COOPERATIVES

Farmer cooperatives are playing a minor role in Panama's agricultural development. Only 31 of the nation's 275 cooperatives in 1972 were classified as agricultural. Many of these are small, undercapitalized,

---

9. Additional information on actions taken during 1971 to improve the market news system can be found in Carl J. Salpietra, Market News-Panama, Ministerio de Agricultura y Ganadería, May 1971, and in Salpietra's progress report published in February 1972.

and inadequately managed. Although national policy is presumed to favor a strong cooperative movement, in practice the movement has lacked strong public sector support.[10]

A federation of agricultural cooperatives (COAGRO) was chartered in December 1969 to assist farm cooperatives in obtaining large-volume purchasing power for supplies to reduce farm input costs and to generate capital for strengthening and expanding the cooperative movement. As originally planned, COAGRO was to develop a field staff to promote cooperative development and assist member cooperatives with training and marketing programs, activities which were to be supported by operating profits and membership fees. The COAGRO program was administered by the National Directorate of Cooperatives (DINACOOP), an administrative agency of MIDA.

Of the approximately 22 agricultural cooperatives eligible for membership in COAGRO, 13 were members at the end of 1972. Active membership in the 13 affiliated cooperatives totaled 1,500 and provided COAGRO with membership fees of approximately B/1,500 annually.

In 1971, COAGRO initiated its farm supply operations with the procurement and distribution of B/344,000 of fertilizers, feed concentrates, chemicals, and seeds, products which were apparently well received. In mid-1971, for example, fertilizer prices in many areas fell by 10% to 15% as independent dealers attempted to remain competitive with COAGRO. After the initial bookings, COAGRO, in an effort to accelerate sales and without full consultation with its affiliates, began to purchase goods for stockage. This independent action alienated many of the affiliates and resulted in inventories of slow-moving supplies. The end result was a reorganization of COAGRO and a revision of its policies.

Viable farmer cooperatives have been identified as a mechanism for providing large numbers of small farmers with production credit.[11] Only five cooperatives have had experience in administering production credit programs. A review of their programs in 1972 suggested that only one of the five had an adequate accounting system, a qualified accountant, and sufficient technical assistance to effectively control their loans. As a result, delinquency rates are high and farmers frequently feel that they are charged too much for services received and need additional technical assistance.

Numerous suggestions have been made for strengthening the agricultural cooperative movement. The following are the major ones:

1. Establish a special cooperative lending department within the new Agricultural Development Bank.
2. Increase government assistance in training programs for cooperatives,

---

10. James E. Pitts, Report and Recommendations on Agricultural Credit Systems in Panama, GOP report, February 1973.
11. Daniels, Agricultural Cooperatives, GOP report, n.d.

especially training in administration, bookkeeping, farm management, and marketing.
3. Assist COAGRO in developing and implementing a program to help
    its affiliates in establishing adequate accounting and credit systems.
4. Concentrate on increasing the membership and improving the man-
    agement of existing cooperatives before initiating programs to sub-
    stantially increase the number of cooperatives.
5. Encourage COAGRO to restrict its farm supply operations to a lim-
    ited number of inputs for direct shipment to affiliates on a limited
    credit basis.
6. Limit production credit for individual cooperatives to pilot programs
    until they demonstrate their ability to control and collect production
    credit loans.

In summary, it appears that few of the agricultural cooperatives
were large enough or financially strong enough in 1973 to undertake
large-scale production credit programs. Training programs for cooperative administrators and government technicians working with cooperatives are considered to be an important first step in strengthening the
cooperative movement. The second step would be to increase the amount
of credit available to cooperatives. Such credit could be used as part of
the third step, increasing the membership of existing cooperatives. A
federation with 20 or 30 strong affiliates could then become an important
element in increasing the total number of agricultural cooperatives.

SUMMARY AND IMPLICATIONS

Perhaps the essential element in accelerating Panama's development
is the commitment of the government to a set of strategies that fully
recognize the role that agricultural development plays in promoting the
growth of nonagricultural sectors of the economy.

A particularly important claimant on public expenditures is agricultural research. Research can generate the possibilities for dramatic
increases in productivity and yields that provide the means for changing
traditional production patterns. Research must also be continuous and
increasing in scale. As new varieties spread and fertilizer use increases,
new problems will arise and new agronomic practices must be developed.

As technical information accumulates, a demand for extension
services of increased competency will be generated. Part of this demand
can be met by private suppliers of farm inputs, but an important part
must be met by government extension services that link the research
organization to the farmers. Unless new technology is available that can
offer high returns to its adopters, however, there will be little payoff
from investments in extension. Such investments can accelerate develop-

ment only when the information extended is productive and profitable for farmers to adopt.

Similar comments apply to agricultural credit. Subsidized credit sometimes has been treated as the requisite for agricultural change. Unfortunately, the credit provided to small farmers often has been diverted to consumption and accumulated as bad debt because there was nothing productive for farmers to purchase. However, there is no reason to believe that small farmers cannot be responsible borrowers where credit is provided for purchases of inputs of proven productivity. If credit and extension programs fail to evoke change, the productivity of the practices being promoted should be evaluated. Cases where highly productive and profitable technology has been tested and proven and made available to farmers along with the requisites for its use and still has not been adopted are difficult to find.

Agricultural education also deserves a prominent place in public sector planning. The shortage of trained agricultural scientists is placing a serious constraint on the nation's development efforts. It takes time to train scientists, to develop successful research programs, and to institute an effective extension service. As the number of well-trained agricultural specialists increases, it will be possible to expand the supervised credit and extension programs. Research programs can be expanded only as rapidly as competent research personnel can be trained. This sequence of events will not occur automatically. It will require foresight on the part of taxpayers, lending institutions, and government officials to recognize changes that are occurring and will continue to occur in the agricultural sector. It also will require a willingness of the people to commit scarce resources to long-term agricultural development programs.

CHAPTER SEVEN

AN AGRICULTURAL SECTOR DEVELOPMENT STRATEGY

DESPITE its rapid economic growth, Panama still faces major economic and social problems due to increasing population and poor utilization of human and natural resources. Total population is projected to reach 1,939,000 by 1980, an increase of nearly 36% over 1970. More than half of all Panamanians live in rural areas or small villages and towns. A wide gap in income and levels of living exists between the comparatively developed urban economy and that portion of the rural population engaged in subsistence agriculture. Agricultural output must increase more rapidly than it has since 1960 if the population is to be fed without substantially higher food prices or increased food imports. How to achieve a high rate of growth in agricultural output while benefiting the majority of the rural population is probably the key policy problem in agriculture.

Labor resources in agriculture are presently underutilized. Underemployment in the agricultural sector, defined as the percentage by which available labor time exceeds labor requirements, was estimated to be nearly 24% in 1971. In other words, the equivalent of approximately 44,000 full-time workers could have been withdrawn from agriculture without reducing output, assuming that those remaining were fully employed. This reduction is approximately equal to the projected migration of male workers from rural to urban locations between 1970 and 1980 provided present trends continue. If the nonagricultural economy continues to absorb labor as rapidly in the 1970s as it did in the 1960s, the agricultural labor force will soon reach its peak and begin to decline. The primary task, then, for the agricultural sector in the 1970s is to achieve substantially higher levels of productivity for its labor force while avoiding the premature release of excess labor.

Panama has adequate natural resources to supply most of its food needs, but they are being underutilized. Less than one-third of the land suitable for farming is being used. Of the land used for farms, less than one-third that is suitable for crops and livestock is being so used; the remaining two-thirds is used for pastures. The carrying capacity of the pastures is approximately one head of livestock per hectare, which is only one-half to one-third the potential carrying capacity if available technology were used. Milk production per cow has been increasing steadily since 1960; but average production in 1970 was still only 2.0 liters daily, which is one-half to one-third the amount that could be obtained from the existing herd if proper feeding and management techniques were widely applied. Average rice yields increased by only 17% between 1961 and 1970, with most of the increase occurring in the late 1960s when the new high-yielding varieties were introduced. Average yield per hectare in 1970 was only 25 quintals of rough rice per hectare, again only one-half to one-third the potential yields. Average corn yield increased by only 11% during the 1960s; bean yields increased by only 7% during the same period. Yields of corn and beans probably were not more than one-half the potential that could be obtained through the use of fertilizer and the introduction of improved varieties.

The low productivity of land resources is reflected in the low per capita incomes of the rural population. In 1970, the average per capita income in rural areas was B/319, compared to B/874 in urban areas. In large part, this difference is due to the lack of both public and private investment in the agricultural sector. Most large landowners have invested relatively little in improving their land. Farmers with 500 and more hectares of land used less than 12% for crops in 1970 and nearly 60% for pastures. Small and medium farmers have not been able to obtain the credit necessary for expansion of landholdings or investment in land and livestock improvement activities. Private banks have directed most of their agricultural credit to export crops (bananas and sugar) and large livestock operations. They have been reluctant to lend to small and medium producers because of the high costs of small loans and the higher risks involved in crop loans, compared to livestock loans. In addition, many small farmers do not hold title to their land and thus cannot provide the loan security that banks require. Public lending agencies have made considerable progress in expanding the amount of short-term production credit available to small and medium farmers, but the amounts available are still far short of the needs. Very little long-term investment credit has been available for small and medium farmers from either private or public lending agencies.

The labor force cannot be held in agriculture without an increase in income flowing from considerable increases in productivity. The increase in productivity should come partly from an increase in land cultivated per man and partly from raising yields per acre. Necessary additional land is available, although investment will be required to bring it into cultivation. Higher yields are a matter of applying modern inputs (improved seed, fertilizers, herbicides, and better cultural practices). The productivity problem is especially acute among small farmers. Achieving a better utilization of agricultural resources constitutes the main agenda for government planning and action.

GOALS AND OBJECTIVES OF AGRICULTURAL DEVELOPMENT

Agricultural development is a management problem of selecting objectives, establishing priorities, and integrating and implementing the components of development programs. In discussing programs and priorities, it is tempting to set forth a list of "essentials" that the government must accomplish. There must be programs of production-oriented research, road building, irrigation and land improvement, market expansion, education and extension, input distribution, credit, price stabilization, and so on. Projects can be elaborated, financed, and implemented in some or all of these areas of action. A prior necessity, however, is a clear understanding and a firm acceptance of the nation's agricultural development goals and objectives. Starting with policies, programs, and projects is a backward approach. Objectives must be specified before priorities can be determined.

The clarification of goals and objectives is an essential first step in the formulation and implementation of development programs. Where goals are confused or incompatible, policies are likely to be uncertain and unproductive. When governments are unable or unwilling to specify the objectives of agricultural development, action programs remain hesitant, ineffective, and filled with self-defeating features.

Panama's development goals have seldom been defined precisely. In general, however, it appears that planning has focused mainly on achieving the highest rate of growth in national output consistent with the nation's capacity to generate investment resources and with a reasonable degree of stability in prices and balance of payments. Increased emphasis is now being given to other goals, many of which are not purely economic but contain a substantial social content. These include creating a more equal income distribution by improving the social, health, and educational services available to all, both in rural and urban areas.

Panama's ability to achieve its social development goals depends to a large extent on its ability to maintain a high rate of growth in national output. If the high national growth rates of the 1960s are to be maintained throughout the 1970s, agricultural output must increase at a rate well above the level achieved in the early seventies. The analysis of sectoral growth rates in Chapter 2 indicates that in order to maintain an annual growth rate in gross domestic product (GDP) of 8% during the 1970s, agricultural output would have to increase by nearly 8% annually, a rate nearly double the average annual growth achieved during the late 1960s.

It is possible to accelerate the growth in agricultural output without concurrent attention to the income distribution and rural levels of living. Production can be generated through programs that make little attempt to benefit the majority of the rural populace. This approach simplifies development planning but does little to transform the traditional sector or to promote development in its broadest sense. The literature on economic development is replete with references to a possible conflict between growth in output and improvements in income distribution. Panama's land base, population distribution, and economic situation, however, are such that the goals of increasing agricultural output and improving the welfare of low-income farmers should be reasonably complementary. Productive lands already are owned by the government and can be opened to development by building new roads. Increasing the credit available to small and medium farmers will allow them to increase their incomes but need not result in a reduction of credit available to large landowners. Enlarging seed improvement and soil testing programs may benefit large and medium farmers relatively more than small farmers but certainly would not reduce the real incomes of small farmers. Expanding agricultural education and technical training programs will benefit farmers in all farm size categories.

The possibility of reconciling production with social welfare and equity goals exists if income redistribution is largely brought about by increasing the productivity of the low-income segment of the agricultural labor force. By following this approach, underemployed farmers can add to their output a contribution to the overall economy while simultaneously improving their economic status.

TARGET GROUPS

Once goals and objectives have been established, it is helpful to identify target groups and to design development programs to meet their needs. A useful approach in Panama's case is to identify the target groups on the basis of farm size. The following major groups (or subsectors) can be identified by this method: (1) a small group of relatively large firms producing major export crops, primarily sugar and bananas; (2) a group consisting of roughly 2,000 to 3,000 large commercial farms that market most of their production and hire most of their labor inputs; (3) a group consisting of some 35,000 small and medium farms that use mostly family labor but market a substantial proportion of their output; and (4) a group of almost 53,000 small farms that are basically subsistence operations on 10 hectares or less and use few if any modern production techniques or inputs. These groups have different problems and require different types of government assistance. Even within a given group, the relevant problems may vary with geographical region so that a program that is appropriate in one location may be unworkable in another.

The Export Subsector

Output of the large-firm export subsector grew at a faster rate than total agricultural output during the 1960s. Output of bananas and plantains increased by 75% between 1960 and 1970, and exports of bananas increased by over 125% during this period. Although the world price of bananas may decline somewhat during the 1970s, banana exports should continue to account for at least 10% of the total value of exports of goods and services in 1980.

Production of sugarcane increased by 184% during the 1960–70 period with most of the increase taking place after 1962, due primarily to the tenfold increase in sugar exports between 1960 and 1970. Panama has the refining capacity and the land resources needed to continue to increase sugar production rapidly throughout the 1970s. Whether it will be profitable to do so depends primarily on world sugar prices and changes in Panama's U.S. sugar quota. As an active participant in the sugar refining industry, the government should develop a thorough understanding of the industry's problems and alternative solutions.

Part of the fishing industry could be included in the export subsector. This industry has grown rapidly and is expected to continue to do so at least until 1980. The fishing industry's primary needs appear to be larger boats and better port facilities. The large boats are being built, but government assistance will be needed if port facilities are to be improved.

The Large-Farm Subsector

The underutilization of land resources by large farms is closely related to the lack of investments in land improvements. Several interrelated factors have influenced the amount and type of investments made by large landowners. An especially important factor is the scarcity of competent farm managers, in part due to the shortcomings of the agricultural education system. Not enough farm youth have been trained in agricultural sciences. Generally speaking, beef cattle operations require less supervision and less farm labor and involve fewer risks than field crop operations. As a result, large landowners invest in cattle rather than in machinery and equipment for planting and harvesting crops. Over time, cattle increase in value and machinery depreciates; the large, commercial farming subsector develops more and better livestock managers than field crop managers; and the lending activities of banks further promote the growth of extensive livestock operations. This circular chain of events cannot be broken without substantial public investment in agricultural education.

Given the existing size structure of farms, less than 300 skilled farm managers would be required to ensure that the 22% of the farmland in farms over 500 hectares was fully and efficiently utilized. If present enrollment levels are maintained, the University of Panama will graduate a total of about 300 persons in agricultural sciences between 1970 and 1985; but many of these graduates will be from and will remain in the Panama City area. Many of them will not be interested in becoming farm managers, and many will be needed by government agencies to help carry out various rural development programs. Obviously, improving the agricultural education system and increasing the number of graduates in agricultural sciences must receive high priority in any program to more fully utilize Panama's land resources.

The investment opportunities outside agriculture are also an important factor influencing the investment decisions of large landowners. Nonagricultural investment opportunities were especially attractive during the 1960s; special tax incentives were available to firms establishing assembly and reexport operations. Urban populations grew rapidly, and average incomes increased by over 80% between 1960 and 1970, thereby creating a rapid growth in the demand for consumer goods and services. The economic growth of urban areas reduced the flow of investment capital to the rural sector, directly by lowering the relative profitability of agricultural investments and indirectly by reducing the amount of bank credit available to farmers.

Government controls of food prices, imports, and exports have had mixed effects on investments in the agricultural sector. The prices of many products have been maintained above world price levels by limiting food imports. Price controls on rice, for example, appear to have been an especially important factor accounting for the increased investments of large farmers in rice production during the late 1960s. The emphasis on price stability, on the other hand, gradually reduced farmer profit margins during the late 1960s and early 1970s as the costs of inputs increased more rapidly than agricultural productivity. In general, however, government price and import controls appear to have been used with reasonable effectiveness to promote economic growth without being used to the long-run disadvantage of either the rural or urban sector.

Steps should be taken also to encourage improved utilization of land on large farms. One of the major purposes of the rural cadastre was to provide information for applying the idle lands provision of the agrarian reform law and for implementing a land tax based on potential productivity. Such policies are difficult to administer but when successful can result in efficient utilization of land by existing landowners.

Medium-Sized Farms

Operators of medium-sized farms probably have been affected more by changes in government agricultural policies than either large or small farmers. Large farmers have a wider range of investment opportunities and greater borrowing ability and are able to transfer funds into and out of the agricultural sector more rapidly than medium farmers. Small farmers use few purchased inputs and market a smaller proportion of their production; consequently, their real incomes are affected less by changes in the market prices of either inputs or outputs. Farmers with 5 to 50 hectares accounted for 45% of the total farms and nearly one-third of the land area in farms in 1970. Only 22% of these farmers held title to their land. Without land titles, there is less incentive to make long-term investments in farm improvements and less opportunity to obtain short-term production loans from banks. The medium farmers would receive considerable benefits from a vigorous program to grant land titles. With land titles to secure short-term loans, these farmers would be in a much better position to utilize new production technology provided by an expanded extension program. The middle-sized farmers are an important and sizable group, yet they seem to have been frequently overlooked in Panama's agricultural development programs. This group of farmers can make a major contribution to output while providing adequate income to hold labor in the agricultural sector.

The Small-Farm Subsector

Farms with 0.5 to 4.9 hectares accounted for 45% of the total farms larger than 0.5 hectares in 1970 but contained only 3.7% of the land area in farms. Most of the farms in this group are subsistence operations using a slash and burn technology. Programs designed to help the families on these farms are needed and should be considered an important part of Panama's social development efforts. Doubling the production on these farms would double the real incomes of over 41,000 farm families that account for about 225,000 persons, roughly 12% of the total population. Since much of the increased production would be consumed on the farm, development programs directed toward farms in this size class probably would have relatively little impact on the total amount of food marketed.

There is no single "best" program for all small farmers. Supervised credit, penetration roads, and land title programs may help some farmers; agricultural cooperatives and asentamientos may be the most effective way to help others. Programs must be designed to meet the needs of the people to be helped.

The total number of small farms in the 0.5 to 4.9 hectare size class declined by about 5% between 1960 and 1970. Further declines are expected, but even if the 1960–70 trend continued, there would still be over 34,000 small farms in this size category at the end of the twentieth century. Based on present family sizes and projected population growth rates, about 6% of the nation's population will be living on small farms (0.5 to 4.9 hectares) in the year 2000 unless vigorous small-farmer assistance programs are undertaken.

The extent to which the current policy of organizing asentamientos to aid the marginal compesinos will be successful is not yet known. The economic importance of the land area in asentamientos is still quite small. Many years will be required to extend this program to the majority of low-income farmers.

The difficulty of working with small farmers is widely recognized. Asentamientos offer one alternative by which groups can be formed to facilitate credit and technical assistance programs. If efficient means can be found to organize asentamientos and develop them into viable economic units, their economic and social contributions can become substantial. On the other hand, if the asentamientos absorb much of the attention and resources of the Ministry of Agricultural Development (MIDA) without achieving economic viability, the opportunity costs of this program may become excessive.

In the long run, the number of small subsistence farmers should diminish. Every effort should be undertaken to encourage creation of employment in the nonfarm economy and to facilitate the entry of small farmers and landless laborers into other occupations. Resettlement and consolidation can assist other small farmers in moving into the medium farm class. A large part of the inefficient utilization of labor in agriculture can be solved only by growth and employment expansion elsewhere in the economy. Nevertheless, good jobs are not automatically available for rural migrants. Little economic or social gain is achieved by moving underemployed rural workers into low-productivity urban service and trade activities. Emphasis on technical education and vocational training is needed to facilitate entry by farm migrants into higher income nonfarm occupations.

PROGRAMS FOR SMALL AND MEDIUM FARMS

The Government of Panama has substantially increased its efforts to assist small and medium farmers in recent years. The responsibilities assigned to MIDA indicate that these efforts will be continued. Most of the standard approaches (credit, extension, coops, etc.) to assisting small and medium farmers have been tried during 1960–70, although many have been used only in small-scale or trial programs. The success of MIDA in helping this group of farmers will depend to a large extent on its ability to enlarge and modify existing programs as well as to develop new ones.

Agricultural credit frequently is considered to be a key factor in encouraging small farmers to adopt new technology. The amount of credit available to small and medium farmers in Panama has grown considerably since 1963. Credit available from public agencies in 1970 accounted for about one-third of total agricultural loans. Government agencies are now the major source of institutional credit for small crop and livestock loans. Even so, in 1970 the National Bank of Panama, Institute of Economic Development (IFE), and Ministry of Agriculture and Livestock (MAG) reported making only 8,296 agricultural loans, which could at most have reached only 10% of the farms with less than 50 hectares. Loans made by the public sector are not classified by farm size, but only 35.4% of the loans made in 1970 were less than B/500. Assuming that all these loans went to small farms, government credit programs reached about 7% of the small farmers with 0.5 to 5 hectares. About two-thirds of the loans of less than B/500 were crop loans of B/100 to B/200 made by MAG.

There is considerable room for expanding agricultural credit programs for small and medium farmers; the question is whether it is worthwhile to do so. The answer depends to a large extent on the objectives of the credit program. If the objective is to increase the level of income of small and medium farmers, the credit programs have made positive contributions toward that goal. Interest rates on credit from public agencies have been lower than those available elsewhere, and repayment times generally are extended more easily than when borrowing from private sources. Using 20% of the value of outstanding loans as the "subsidy element" of public agency loan programs, the average borrower in 1970 received a B/330 credit subsidy. If only IFE and MAG loans are considered, the average credit subsidy per borrower was approximately B/230; the B/100 difference is due to the higher proportion of large loans made by the National Bank. Assuming an average family size of 5.5 persons, the average income of a rural family in 1970 was approximately B/1,750. A B/230 credit subsidy would represent a 13% increase in real income for the average farm family receiving a loan from IFE or MAG in 1970. On this basis, the total subsidy of IFE and MAG agricultural credit programs in 1970 was about B/1.5 million, roughly 1% of the total income of families living on farms in the 0.5 to 50 hectare size categories.

Different criteria must be used if the goal of the agricultural credit programs is to increase the productivity of the land resources used by small farmers. Some increases in production are reported in cases where credit is used for the purchase of fertilizer, but there is little evidence to indicate that soil testing is used to ensure purchase of an appropriate fertilizer. Much of the crop credit is used to clear and prepare land for crops that are then grown with traditional technology. Many borrowers have little contact with extension agents, and very little actual supervised credit is involved in farm planning. Although no detailed quantitative studies have been made, the general program evaluations available suggest it is unlikely that the credit programs have increased crop yields or livestock productivity by an average of more than 10% for those farmers who have received credit. There is also little evidence of a positive demonstration effect for farmers not receiving credit. In terms of total impact in 1970, government credit programs probably did not increase the total output of farmers with 0.5 to 50 hectares by more than 1% at most.

The limited impact of credit programs on the productivity of small farmers is sometimes attributed to the lack of vehicles or funds to allow credit agents and extension personnel to visit and work with farmers. The shortage of well-trained farm management technicians willing to work as credit or extension agents is also cited as an important reason for the lack of on-farm supervision of small-farm loans. The shortage of well-qualified credit and extension agents probably has been and will continue to be the key factor limiting the successful growth of small-farm credit programs.

Numerous changes in administrative procedures have been suggested for increasing the efficiency and effectiveness of the credit and extension agents. Among the suggestions most frequently made are (1) to allow regional offices greater responsibility in approving loans, (2) to simplify the process of screening applicants and approving loans, and (3) to encourage the development of small-farmer credit cooperatives. Most of the proposed changes in administrative procedures would result in more loan approvals per credit agent and would increase the subsidy element of public credit programs but probably would have little impact on increasing the productivity of the farmers receiving loans. The suggested changes are certainly worthwhile; but even if they increased the effectiveness of field personnel by as much as 25%, the existing programs still would not reach more than one-eighth of the small and medium farmers.

These measurements appear to judge the small farmer credit program too harshly. A 10% subsidy, plus a 10% productivity increase, translates into a 20% increase in real income of the average borrower. New farmers participate in the loan programs over time so that more than 10% of the small and medium farmers are affected by the program, even though only 10% may benefit from the program in any given year. The credit programs are worthwhile and should be expanded. Apparently, during the 1960s, the programs were expanded as rapidly as qualified people could be hired and perhaps more rapidly than these people could be given support in the form of vehicles to reach farmers and technological packages that were acceptable. The main point is that even if the public agency credit program is doubled in size by 1980, it would still not be reaching more than about 25% of the small and medium farmers in any given year; the credit programs therefore need to be supplemented with other types of programs if more farmers are to be reached.

Indeed, the question of how many farmers can be reached with programs designed to provide the services and support necessary for economically viable production is critical. The government, by necessity, must concentrate its programs on farmers with sufficient land and other resources to permit them to benefit from the new technology. Acceptance of this necessity should provide a basis for defining a strategy for small-farm development leading to better coordination and improved performance of assistance programs.

COLONIZATION PROGRAMS

Spontaneous colonization of new land is occurring throughout Panama, especially in the provinces of Bocas del Toro, Darien, Colon, and Panama. The colonos are mostly small farmers and landless laborers from Chiriqui, Veraguas, Herrera, Los Santos, and Cocle who locate where rivers or new roads provide access to new lands. In most of these areas, the colonos find themselves in circumstances similar to their previous locations. Land is cleared indiscriminately; farmers lack legal title; marketing is difficult; credit and technical assistance are not available; and production is largely for subsistence purposes.

More land for settlement will become available as construction of new roads is completed in Panama, Darien, and Bocas del Toro. Most of this land is owned by the government. These new lands can be used to provide opportunities for small subsistence farmers to establish viable economic units. A systematic pattern of utilization of these new areas is unlikely to take place, however, unless the government establishes a policy regulating land use.

The Agrarian Reform Commission has resettled 7,268 families on public lands or private farms acquired under the agrarian code. The unanswered questions about colonization and settlement are numerous. How costly will large-scale settlement programs be in the new areas in Panama and Darien provinces? How large should farms be to achieve desired income levels and to protect natural resources? What additional infrastucture investments and services will be necessary for successful colonization? These questions must be answered to define the potential and priorities for colonization and resettlement in the future.

The role of colonization programs in meeting output and welfare goals in the agriculture sectors should be considered carefully. Spontaneous colonization, in the absence of infrastructure investment and provision of credit and technical assistance, simply shifts subsistence agriculture from one location to another. How rapidly will these new lands become available? How many economically sized farm units can be formed in them? What investments in infrastructure and services will be necessary? Little information to answer these important questions is now available, but answers are needed to determine the role of colonization in the future development of the sector.

FORESTRY AND LAND USE POLICIES

The need to enforce existing land policies and to develop more comprehensive ones is clearly evident. Valuable land resources are being lost through erosion. There are no well-defined and enforced water control programs. Forests are being destroyed by subsistence farmers who have little knowledge of the agricultural potential of the land they clear or the role that forests play in regulating water flows. The short-run view that Panama has adequate land resources to meet its long-run needs fails to take into account the increasing rate at which farmland and forests are being destroyed.

The opening of the Darien region and expanded programs of colonization and resettlement will increase the need to enforce existing forest resources policies. Much of the basic information needed to develop an enforceable forest management program is now available because of the reconnaissance inventories of forest resources and the cadastral survey undertaken during the 1960s.

Two basic steps must be taken in formulating a forest management policy. First, it must be determined which areas should be used permanently for agriculture and which for forestry. Second, the permanent forestlands must be classified according to their forestry use (production, protection, recreation, etc.). The need for such classification is recognized in the Forest Resources Law of 1966.

Results of the inventories of forest resources show that commercially productive forest is primarily the area presently classified as humid tropical forest. This forest type is found mainly in the eastern section of the country in Panama and Darien provinces and forms approximately one-half of the remaining forests or one-quarter of the nation's total land area. This region of humid tropical forest includes most of the remaining forested land area suited for permanent agriculture.

The potential conflict between forestry and agriculture in the humid tropical forest areas could be minimized in the following manner:

1. The areas of better soils in the main river basins of Darien province could be deforested and devoted to high production agriculture, a policy that will serve to channel both government and private coloni-

zation efforts away from the permanent forest areas in the eastern region of Panama. Efforts should be made, however, to preserve the more valuable stands of cativo (Spanish walnut) for forestry purposes.

2. The remaining forests of Panama and Darien provinces, totaling 10,000 square kilometers, are located in areas with poorer soils and broken topography where any form of agriculture would be low yielding and marginal in nature. This area should be maintained as the main production forest. It is estimated that this will be adequate to maintain the national forest industry at its present level of extraction. In addition to providing timber production, this forest will provide a catchment area for Bayano Dam and could be used as a sanitary zone adjacent to the border with Colombia to provide protection against hoof-and-mouth disease.

3. The remaining areas of potential production forest are smaller and are scattered throughout the rest of the country. With the exception of the mangroves and orey swamp forests, they are much more vulnerable to agricultural colonization than the forests in the more isolated eastern region of the country. Although these forests cover a total of approximately 16,000 square kilometers, much of this area will eventually be lost to colonization and subsistence farming. The speed with which this occurs will depend to a large extent on the government's efforts to promote colonization in other areas of the country.

The wetter upland areas of Panama and Darien provinces and much of the Atlantic Coast area are unsuited to commercially productive forests. These areas include nearly one-half the remaining forests of the country. Actual and potential marketable volumes in these forests are so low that it seems unlikely the high extraction expenses will ever be justified. The marketable volumes of timber do not justify the establishment of secondary and feeder roads in most areas. These areas also are unsuited for agriculture; even extensive grazing would be a marginal activity. Such forests should be closed to colonization and maintained for the protection of soil and water.

Several forest areas are well suited for national park purposes, for recreational areas, and for development of the tourist industry. Among the most important areas in this category are Volcan Baru, Portobelo, Altos de Campana, and Islas de las Perlas.

Some deforested areas should be returned to forestry use. The difference between the area of forest identified by the reconnaissance inventories and the statistics on land in agricultural use suggests that approximately 10,000 square kilometers could be classified as wasteland. The main wasteland area is located on the southern slopes of the Cordillera Central, primarily in the very humid forests of this area. The combination of climate, soil, and topography has ensured that agricultural practices following deforestation have failed mainly because of soil deterioration.

Some areas have been classified as "agricultural zones for erosion protection." Here, agriculture can be practiced provided there is some reforestation and appropriate measures are taken to control soil erosion. Two of the most important areas where this should be encouraged are (1) the catchment area of the Rio Chargres and Lago Madden, which is an important source of drinking water for the Panama City–Colon area as well as a source of water used in the operation of the Panama Canal locks, and (2) the highlands of Chiriqui province.

Most of the reforestation should be for protection purposes rather than for timber production. This end can be accomplished most easily simply by protecting the area against fire and grazing and allowing the natural vegetation to return slowly.

The Forest Resources Law of 1966 was the first reasonably comprehensive forestry legislation. It contains both statements of policy and legislation designed to regulate forestry activities. The data contained in the reconnaissance inventories completed since 1966 will allow the existing law to be revised and improved.[1] Government ability to enforce the law will depend to a large extent on whether competent specialists in forestry management can be attracted and retained.

The protective function of the highland forests along the southern slopes of the Cordillera Central is especially important in light of the limited prospects for developing large-scale irrigation systems for regulating water flows in the central and western provinces. Most of the large-scale irrigation projects that have been investigated since 1960 do not appear to be economically justified. Trends in world food prices could change this situation but an additional five to ten years time would be required to complete the planning, financing, and construction of the proposed projects.

IRRIGATION PROGRAMS

Approximately 14,000 hectares of irrigated land are in small-scale irrigation systems, primarily in Chiriqui and Cocle provinces. Most of the existing irrigation systems have been constructed by private individuals or companies. Government-sponsored irrigation systems account for approximately 2,000 of the 14,000 irrigated hectares. Eight large farms have constructed irrigation systems for pastureland since 1967 (between 1967 and 1973), but most private systems are used for high-value crops, primarily sugarcane, bananas and other fruit, vege-

---

1. Additional information on Panama's forestry resources and specific suggestions for revising the Forest Resources Law of 1966 can be found in George Conn, Panamá, Inventariación y Demostraciones Forestales, FAO report, Rome, 1972.

tables, tobacco, and rice. Nearly all the present irrigation systems now utilize available river water to provide supplemental irrigation during dry periods. It is estimated that the cost of pumps and canals for recently constructed systems is usually less than B/500 per hectare.[2]

Feasibility or prefeasibility studies have been completed on six irrigation projects since 1963, large-scale systems that would utilize the basins of the rivers La Villa, Santa Maria, Grande-Chico, Zarati, Tonosi, and Chiriqui-Chico. A total of approximately 90,000 hectares would be irrigated if all six projects were in full operation. The various studies indicate that at least 200,000 hectares in the main agricultural areas could be irrigated with gravity systems utilizing rainwater, which is approximately the amount of land used for annual crops in 1970. Some studies suggest that there also is considerable potential for irrigating additional land with subterranean water.

The total cost of construction and land preparation for the large-scale irrigation projects ranges from approximately B/400 to over B/1,600 per hectare. Irrigation projects for the rivers Chiriqui-Chico, La Villa, and Guarare all have costs of B/600 or less per irrigated hectare. The benefit-cost ratio for the first phase of the Chiriqui-Chico project has been estimated to be 3.6. Most of the other projects have benefit-cost ratios in the 3.0 to 3.3 range.

It appears that much additional analysis will be needed before undertaking any of the large-scale irrigation projects. Studies completed prior to 1965 need to be updated. The cost estimates in several of the studies completed after 1965 appear to be unusually low. The initial (1963) study on the Rio La Villa project, for example, indicated a total cost of B/1,600 per hectare while the 1971 study on the same project estimated the cost to be only B/430 per hectare. The benefit-cost ratios for the studies generally assumed that market prices would not be affected by the increased output resulting from the use of irrigated land, an assumption that is reasonable only for exported products, primarily sugarcane and meat. The majority of the studies recommended the production of irrigated rice and vegetables, which have seldom been exported. Substantial increases in the production of rice and vegetables would force farm prices down and thereby reduce the benefits of the irrigation projects.

Several of the large-scale irrigation projects may eventually become economically feasible and may be implemented. Meanwhile, it would appear advisable to encourage the development of small-scale, low-cost irrigation systems that may be incorporated into the larger irrigation and water control projects at a later date. In this way, both farmers and government technicians will gain experience in irrigated farming, and

---

2. Reinmar Tejeira, Aspectos del Riego en Panamá, Asesoría Técnica, S.A., Panama City, June 1973.

more accurate information can be gathered on the yield increases to be expected.

Colonization, forestry management, and irrigation are but three of the topics that need be considered in developing national land use policies. The formulation of land policy must take place within a general framework of public action. In a broad sense, land policies are social control measures designed to improve the use of land resources and the conditions of property rights under which people work and live on the land. The main problems to which land policy is addressed, therefore, lie in the fields of land use, conservation, development, and tenure. The objectives of land policy are governed by what people desire and what the functions of government are conceived to be in bringing about better land use and tenure. Panama appears to be in the initial stages of formulating more definite land use policies. Public interest in the agricultural sector has increased considerably since the mid-1960s. Much of the basic data for formulating specific policies and programs has been collected. There is evidence of an increased realization of the need to improve land tenure arrangements and to ensure the long-run productivity of the nation's land and forest resources. Continued growth in the nonagricultural sector will ease formulation and implementation of more comprehensive land policies within the 1970–80 decade.[3]

AGRICULTURAL EDUCATION AND RESEARCH

The rate at which Panama can effectively increase government expenditures on agricultural development programs is basically limited by the rate at which capable agricultural technicians can be trained. Based on the levels of efficiency and staffing of the public sector in 1972, a 10% increase in expenditures on agricultural development programs would require approximately 80 additional agricultural technicians. Thirty of these would be ingenieros agrónomos and 50 would be bachilleres agropecuarios.

The two principal technical schools for agriculture, the National Agricultural Institute (INA) and Felix Olivares, graduate about 100 bachilleres agropecuarios annually. The University of Panama has averaged about 15 ingenieros agrónomos annually and is unlikely to increase the number of graduates to more than 18 during 1974–79.

From this viewpoint, the number of ingenieros agrónomos graduated annually appears to be the most serious bottleneck to increasing the size and effectiveness of the government's agricultural development programs. Assuming no changes in the efficiency of government em-

---

3. A variety of viewpoints on the many dimensions of land use programs and policies can be found in John F. Timmons and William G. Murray, eds., *Land Problems and Policies,* Ames, Iowa State University Press, 1950.

ployees, the government could not effectively increase the size of its agricultural programs by more than about 5% to 6% annually, even if it could hire all of the ingenieros agrónomos graduated each year. Trying to increase the size of the programs more rapidly would require heavier reliance on less adequately trained personnel and probably a corresponding reduction in program effectiveness. The need for more and better trained agricultural technicians has been recognized widely, but the implications of the long lead times required to train such technicians adequately appear to have been overlooked.

Any program to increase the number of agricultural specialists must start in the rural areas, not in Panama City. The logical starting point is in technical high schools such as INA. Enrollment increases in the technical high schools will lead within three years to an increased number of rural area students entering the College of Agriculture; therefore, the expansion program proposed for INA, if started in 1974, would begin to affect enrollments in the College of Agriculture by 1977. If INA's enrollment were doubled and graduating classes increased by 50 students, the result would be an additional 20 to 25 students from INA entering the College of Agriculture annually. The expansion program for INA, if started in 1974, would provide graduating classes of 90 to 100 students by about 1979–80. With a total graduating class of 90 to 100 students, INA could provide about 30% of the first-year students needed by the College of Agriculture to double the size of its teaching program.

Anticipating these enrollment increases, the College of Agriculture could begin a building program in 1974 and start to enlarge its faculty and staff in 1976. A scholarship program for advanced training abroad in agricultural sciences, if begun in 1974, would provide new faculty personnel with M.S. degrees by 1976 and personnel with Ph.D. degrees by 1978. Following this time schedule, the graduating classes of the College of Agriculture could be increased to about 50 students by about 1982.

Expansion and increased coordination of existing research programs are worthwhile objectives. Increased coordination is possible without program expansion and could be accomplished by the establishment of a National Agricultural Research Committee made up primarily of personnel from the University of Panama and various government agencies. The committee's initial objective would be to keep the various research groups fully informed on what research is under way, what is being learned from the research, and how the findings are being used. Plans for substantially expanding research could be initiated once an increased number of Panamanians are enrolled in advanced training programs abroad. If an advanced studies scholarship program were initiated in 1974, for example, a five-year program to establish a research institute could be started in 1976 with the expectation that an increased number of well-trained research specialists would be available by 1978. The establishment of such an institute could be a second, intermediate objective of a National Agricultural Research Committee.

The types of agricultural research needed are likely to change considerably. More sociological research regarding the types of organizations and extension programs most likely to help small farmers will be needed, and the importance of production problems of the Darien region will increase. Research related to fertilizer use, soil management, water control, and cropping patterns will have to be expanded.

By the late 1970s, it should be possible to broaden the extension programs to place more emphasis on farm management, marketing farm products, and machinery maintenance. Promoting the use of improved seed, proper cultivation practices, weed and insect controls, and soil testing should be continued, but the basic fundamentals should be familiar to an increased percentage of the farmers by 1980. Changing the emphasis of extension programs will not require substantial changes in teaching programs at technical high schools or the College of Agriculture. These schools already offer courses in agricultural economics, farm management, agricultural marketing, and farm accounting. Some changes may be needed in the topics covered in these courses, but they can be introduced gradually.

It may be possible to increase the efficiency and effectiveness of government employees through on-the-job training, changes in administrative procedures, short-term training scholarships, increases in support facilities (vehicles, office equipment, etc.), and reorganizations. It is hoped that efforts in these areas could increase overall efficiency by at least 4% to 5% annually. Numerous changes in administrative procedures were suggested by specialists working with the agricultural Sector Study Commission (SSC). The reorganization of the Ministry of Agriculture should result in a more rational allocation of scarce technical talent. Short-term training programs have been well received by government technicians and appear to have been highly effective in increasing the general level of expertise within government agencies. Such training programs complement the more formal, longer term programs of the University of Panama.

AN AGRICULTURAL DEVELOPMENT STRATEGY

Defining an agricultural development strategy is a continuous process. The research undertaken by the SSC provides a basis for identifying many specific programs and projects and estimating their potential contribution to national objectives. The basic studies listed in the bibliography contain many specific suggestions for improving the implementation of programs as well as many insights into which programs have worked well and why. Nevertheless, in a real sense, serious sector analysis has only begun. There is a need to institutionalize a planning and analytical capability so that sector analysis can be organized as a continuous activity.

The analysis of future growth prospects presented in Chapter 1 indicates that a continued growth in real income of 7% to 8% annually is a feasible target during the 1970s. If such high growth rates are achieved, the result will be rapid changes in the structure of the economy and a need to continually revise agricultural development strategies.

By the late 1970s, the opening of the Darien region could substantially change the distribution of the rural population and the priorities assigned to various commodities. If the Darien Highway is completed by 1980, the construction program alone will contribute at least B/10 million annually to the gross domestic product (GDP). The construction costs in this case would account for approximately a 1% annual increase in GDP.[4] Government and private investments in land improvements, buildings, schools, and social infrastructure in the Darien region could increase the growth rate of GDP by an additional 1%. Approximately 60% of the estimated B/100 million cost of the Darien Highway project is to be grant funded. Assuming an average annual inflow of B/10 million over a six-year period, the grant funding is equivalent to an increase in the export of goods and services of approximately 3% annually. The results of the macroeconomic model estimated in Chapter 2 indicate that an additional B/10 million in annual "exports" would increase total imports by B/4,650,000. Food imports in 1971 constituted approximately 10% of total imports. Using this percentage, an additional B/10 million in "exports" would increase food imports by B/465,000, which is less than 0.5% of the total value of agricultural output in 1970.

Increased exports of goods and services was the single most important factor in the growth rate of the economy during the 1960s. Agricultural and fishery exports increased from less than B/20 million in 1960 to over B/80 million in 1970. Nearly all the increased food exports were accounted for by bananas, seafoods, and sugar. Banana exports, for example, increased from B/11,640,000 in 1960 to B/60,831,000 in 1970 and accounted for over 80% of the total increase in food exports. More attention will need to be given to bananas, seafoods, and sugar in future studies of the agricultural sector.

The role of cattle production in Panama's development has been clarified in the studies prepared for the SSC. All the studies on cattle production and marketing emphasized the extensive nature of beef production and the need to modernize the meat marketing system; many stressed the potential of beef exports as a source of foreign exchange. Cattle production obviously is an important aspect of agriculture. Over 60% of the institutional credit for agriculture, excluding credit for sugar

---

4. The government investment multiplier estimated in Chapter 2 is 0.9717. See Table 2.1.

and bananas, goes to livestock, primarily cattle. Beef and milk accounted for about 38% of the value of farm output in 1971. Meat is second to cereals as a source of protein in the average diet. Together, meat and milk account for nearly one-third of the average daily consumption of protein and nearly 12% of the calories consumed daily. Over 50% of the agricultural land is used for pastures.

There are still many unanswered questions concerning the livestock industry. First, to what extent is the credit going to livestock producers actually being used within the agricultural sector to improve the productivity of the land and livestock on cattle farms? Secondly, how would alternative programs to increase beef exports affect the income distribution of the rural sector? Beef exports presently account for less than 3% of food exports and less than 1% of the total exports of goods and services. At most, some 2,000 farmers produce nearly all the exported beef. The projections of exportable surpluses discussed in Chapter 4 suggest that the relative importance of beef exports is unlikely to increase by 1980 unless world prices continue to increase and domestic prices are allowed to adjust upward toward world price levels. A wide variety of tax and subsidy systems have not yet been investigated and could be used to promote cattle production, to increase the productivity of land now utilized for pasture, and to improve the income distribution of the rural sector.

An important function of a continuing sector study would be to provide an improved data base for evaluating the effects of a sector development program. Without baseline data and consistent collection of information over time, it is almost impossible to measure the real economic effects of a development program on farmers, marketing agencies, and consumers.

Results of agricultural sector analysis vividly illustrate the uniqueness of Panama's development situation. Services account for over two-thirds of the nation's export earnings. The value of food imports in 1970 was less than one-third the value of food exports. Food imports as a percentage of GDP were only 2.2% in 1970, compared to 3.2% in 1960. Panama is hardly a major food importer and in a broad sense is self-sufficient in food production. The supply and demand projections presented in Chapter 4 indicate that the total value of food imports probably will continue to increase, but if Panama is able to maintain the overall growth rate of GDP at 7% to 8% annually, food imports should continue to be less than 4% to 5% of GDP at most. In this case, the government will continue to have considerable flexibility in regulating food prices. This ability is increased further by the concentrated nature of the food marketing channels. Government price policies thereby become an extremely important tool for promoting (or discouraging) the production of basic foods, perhaps the single most powerful tool presently available. Emphasis on price stability, however, has reduced the government's willingness to use price policy as a development tool.

Panama's orientation toward export of services and its self-sufficiency in food production has resulted, in the past, in a general unconcerned attitude toward agricultural development. Improvements in the road system during the 1950s linked the central and western provinces more closely to Panama City, helped keep food prices low, and encouraged private investment in the agricultural sector. The decline in banana production during the 1950s and the resulting relocation of the banana industry began to increase public interest in agriculture by the early 1960s. The possibilities of increasing sugar production and of becoming self-sufficient in rice production through the introduction of the green revolution rice varieties as well as the recovery of the banana industry based on new varieties grown in a new location resulted in further increases in public interest and private investment in the agricultural sector by the mid-1960s and an agricultural boom in the late 1960s. The formation of MAG as a separate government agency in 1969 reflected both the increased recognition of the importance of the agricultural sector and the increased public concern for the welfare of the majority of the nation's population living in rural areas.

The rapid changes that have taken place in the agricultural sector during 1960–70 have called forth equally rapid changes in government policies and programs. The lack of basic information on the agricultural sector has made it difficult not only for government agencies to anticipate the impact of various programs but also for the general public and international development agencies to fully understand what was happening and why. The shortage of well-trained agricultural technicians, due partly to the earlier unconcerned attitude toward agriculture, has made it difficult for the government to increase its development programs as rapidly, efficiently, and effectively as desired.

The slower rate of growth of the agricultural sector since 1970 is partly due to the world market situation for bananas, to weather conditions, and to an adjustment in priorities, with more emphasis being placed on improving the welfare of low-income farmers and less on short-run increases in food output. The slower rate of growth in food production has resulted in upward pressures on food prices and increased food imports. In a sense, the urban sector is now being asked to return to farmers a few of the benefits of low food prices that urban workers enjoyed during the 1960s. This policy is consistent with the basic conclusion of the agricultural sector analysis that a substantial increase in the productivity of the existing agricultural labor force should be the major public policy objective of 1970–80. This should come partly from increasing the area cultivated, especially by small and medium farmers, and partly from yield-increasing technology.[5]

---

5. Specific proposals for increasing the production and income of low-income and medium-income farmers are discussed in Edward J. Wellhausen, A Proposal for a National Program in Rural Development Focused Primarily on Improving the Income and General Welfare of the Subsistence of Semi-commercial Farmers and Underemployed Rural Laborers in Panama, GOP report, April 1973.

If this objective is achieved, the agricultural sector should not experience premature losses of its labor force. At the same time, jobs must be created in nonfarm occupations and training must be provided for the steady stream of rural migrants that is necessary to hold the agricultural labor force to its current level or permit it to begin to decrease.

For those remaining in agriculture, increases in productivity will redistribute income and also create a larger rural demand for nonfarm goods and services. By raising the productivity of farm labor, overall economic development will be aided and improved living conditions in rural areas will be achieved.

PANAMA'S POPULATION AND LABOR FORCE

CHANGES in the population of Panama since 1950 are shown in Table A.1. Population projections to 1980 and 1990 given in the table were made on the assumption that the rate of growth will continue at the 3.1% per year registered in the 1960s. If this assumption is valid, the population of Panama will number around 2 million persons by 1980.

The distribution of the population by province and sector in 1960 and 1970 is given in Table A.2. Panama province is the most heavily populated, and its share of the total population has been increasing. Chiriqui is next largest in terms of population size, followed by Veraguas, Colon, and Cocle. The provinces with the smallest populations are Darien and Bocas del Toro.

In 1970, 48% of the population was classified as urban. This classification, however, counts cities or towns of 1,500 inhabitants or more having minimum basic services as urban. The urban population increased by 50% in the 1960–70 period, compared to an increase in the rural population of slightly less than 20%. The main concentration of population is contained in the metropolitan areas defined as the cities of Panama and Colon and the area on either side of the Canal Zone.

Basic information on the economically active population, employment, and unemployment are contained in Table A.3 for the 1960–70 period. The national unemployment rate is about 7% of the work force. In the metropolitan area, however, 10% or more of the labor force is unemployed.

TABLE A.1. ● **POPULATION GROWTH, 1940–70, AND PROJECTIONS, 1980–90**

Year	Population
1940	622,576
1950	805,285
1960	1,075,541
1970	1,428,082
1980[a]	1,939,000
1990[a]	2,620,200

Source: Panamá en Cifras, November 1972, p. 10.

[a]Projected assuming that the 3.1% rate of population growth continues.

TABLE A.2. ● DISTRIBUTION OF THE POPULATION BY PROVINCE AND SECTOR, 1960 AND 1970

Province	1960		1970	
	000 persons	%	000 persons	%
Total	1,075.5	100.0	1,428.1	100.0
Bocas del Toro	32.6	3.0	43.5	3.0
Cocle	93.2	8.7	118.0	8.3
Colon	105.4	9.8	134.3	9.4
Chiriqui	188.3	17.5	236.2	16.5
Darien	19.7	1.8	22.7	1.6
Herrera	61.7	5.7	72.5	5.1
Los Santos	70.5	6.6	72.4	5.1
Panama	372.4	34.6	576.7	40.4
Veraguas	131.7	12.3	151.8	10.6
Subtotal, Urban	446.2	41.5	679.4	47.6
Subtotal, Rural	629.3	58.5	748.7	52.4
Subtotal, Metropolitan Area	430.4	40.0	600.9	42.1
Subtotal, Rest of the Republic	645.1	60.0	827.2	52.9

Source: Dirección de Estadística y Censo.

205

TABLE A.3. • EMPLOYMENT AND ECONOMICALLY ACTIVE POPULATION, 1960–70

Year	Employment [a] (000 persons)	Economically Active [a] (000 persons)	Unemployment (000 persons)	Rate of Unemployment (%)
1960	300	330	30.0	9.1
1963	339	360	21.0	5.8
1964	338	365	27.0	7.4
1965	350	379	29.0	7.7
1966	371	391	20.0	5.1
1967	384	409	25.0	6.1
1968	404	435	31.0	7.1
1969	420	450	30.0	6.7
1970	433	466	33.3	7.1

Source: Estadística Panameña, Series "0."

[a]Refers to persons 15 years of age and older.

MATRICES FOR
INPUT-OUTPUT MODEL

TABLE B.1. • D MATRIX FOR THE INPUT-OUTPUT MODEL

1	1.1183	0.0	0.0	0.0	0.0	0.0	0.0	0.0	0.0	0.0
2	0.0	1.2963	0.0	0.0	0.0	0.0	0.0	0.0	0.0	0.0
3	0.0	0.0	1.3950	0.0	0.0	0.0	0.0	0.0	0.0	0.0
4	0.0	0.0	0.0	2.8000	0.0	0.0	0.0	0.0	0.0	0.0
5	0.0	0.0	0.0	0.0	1.0000	0.0	0.0	0.0	0.0	0.0
6	0.0	0.0	0.0	0.0	0.0	1.0000	0.0	0.0	0.0	0.0
7	0.0	0.0	0.0	0.0	0.0	0.0	1.0000	0.0	0.0	0.0
8	0.0	0.0	0.0	0.0	0.0	0.0	0.0	1.0000	0.0	0.0
9	0.0	0.0	0.0	0.0	0.0	0.0	0.0	0.0	1.0	0.0
10	0.0	0.0	0.0	0.0	0.0	0.0	0.0	0.0	0.0	1.0

TABLE B.2. • A MATRIX FOR THE INPUT-OUTPUT MODEL

1	0.0773	0.0	0.2553	0.0130	0.0	0.0	0.0	0.0	0.0	0.0
2	0.0001	0.0013	0.0016	0.0093	0.0188	0.0	0.0	0.0	0.0	0.0
3	0.0094	0.0	0.1002	0.0148	0.0	0.0	0.0	0.0	0.0	0.0
4	0.0385	0.0492	0.0579	0.1795	0.3429	0.1805	0.0720	0.0180	0.0010	0.0250
5	0.0	0.0	0.0	0.0	0.0	0.0	0.0	0.0	0.0	0.0
6	0.0002	0.0007	0.0111	0.0147	0.0079	0.0273	0.0211	0.0079	0.0006	0.0265
7	0.0490	0.0247	0.1020	0.1893	0.0559	0.0980	0.0079	0.0184	0.0082	0.0159
8	0.0066	0.0	0.0039	0.0060	0.0014	0.0005	0.0362	0.0182	0.0002	0.0075
9	0.0003	0.0011	0.0027	0.0071	0.0004	0.0010	0.0302	0.0059	0.0	0.0170
10	0.0020	0.0031	0.0135	0.0123	0.0023	0.0313	0.0184	0.1130	0.0002	0.0299

TABLE B.3. ● (I–A)⁻ MATRIX FOR THE INPUT-OUTPUT MODEL

1	0.9626	0.0002	0.1901	0.0059	0.0021	0.0011	0.0005	0.0001	0.0	0.0002
2	0.0002	0.7723	0.0011	0.0028	0.0155	0.0005	0.0002	0.0001	0.0	0.0001
3	0.0072	0.0002	0.7740	0.0044	0.0016	0.0009	0.0003	0.0001	0.0	0.0001
4	0.0160	0.0153	0.0235	0.3845	0.1345	0.0748	0.0301	0.0097	0.0007	0.0125
5	0.0	0.0	0.0	0.0	1.0000	0.0	0.0	0.0	0.0	0.0
6	0.0018	0.0014	0.0118	0.0077	0.0122	1.0328	0.0235	0.0122	0.0008	0.0289
7	0.0518	0.0224	0.0951	0.0752	0.0841	0.1172	1.0175	0.0240	0.0085	0.0222
8	0.0085	0.0009	0.0081	0.0052	0.0054	0.0056	0.0379	1.0204	0.0005	0.0088
9	0.0021	0.0017	0.0055	0.0052	0.0041	0.0058	0.0316	0.0089	1.0003	0.0184
10	0.0043	0.0032	0.0146	0.0072	0.0068	0.0372	0.0249	0.1198	0.0005	1.0334

GLOSSARY

AID. Agency for International Development

BID. Inter-American Development Bank (Banco Interamericano de Desarrollo)

CISA. Sector Study Commission (Comisión para la Intergración del Sector Agropecuario, see SSC)

COAGRO. Federation of Agricultural Cooperatives

DINACOOP. National Directorate of Cooperatives

FAO. Food and Agriculture Organization of the United Nations

GOP. Government of Panama

IBRD. International Bank for Reconstruction and Development (World Bank)

IDB. Inter-American Development Bank

IFE. Institute of Economic Development (Instituto de Fomento Económico)

IICA. Inter-American Institute of Agricultural Sciences (Instituto Interamericano de Ciencias Agricolas)

INA. National Agricultural Institute (Instituto Nacional de Agricultura)

MAG. Ministry of Agriculture and Livestock (Ministerio de Agricultura y Ganadería, became MIDA in 1973)

MIDA. Ministry of Agricultural Development (Ministerio de Desarrollo Agropecuario, was MAG prior to 1973)

MPPE. Ministry of Economic Planning and Policy (Ministerio de Planificación y Política Económica, formerly Dirección General de Planificación y Administración de la Presidencia)

OEA. Organization of American States (Organización de los Estados Americanos)

SSC. Sector Study Commission (also referred to as CISA)

UN. United Nations

BIBLIOGRAPHY

Adams, Kermit. Preliminary Report on Instituto Nacional de Agricultura—Dr. Augusto Samuel Boyd, Divisa, Panama. Report prepared for CISA, Republic of Panama, March 1972. 82 pages.

Agnew, Donald B. Economic Feasibility Study for Additional Cattle Slaughter Facilities in the Republic of Panama. Report prepared for MIDA, Republic of Panama, February 1972. 37 pages.

Aizpurua, Jaime. Problemas, Situación Actual y Posibles Soluciones de la Actividad Ganadera en Panamá. Report prepared for CISA, Republic of Panama, December 1971. 95 pages.

Battles, Ralph. An Agricultural Credit Program for Panama. Report prepared for MIDA, Republic of Panama, February 1973. 21 pages.

Breitenbach, Charles. Development of an Action Program to Systematically Achieve an Expanded Production of Basic Cereal and Leguminous Grains in Panama. Report prepared for MIDA. Republic of Panama, February 1973. 43 pages.

Chavez, Daniel H. Panama, Manpower Supply and Demand in the Agricultural Sector of the Economy. Report prepared for CISA, Republic of Panama, August 1972. 28 pages.

Chen, Angel M. Costos de Producción de Hortalizas en las Tierras Altas de Chiriquí y en las Provincias Centrales. Report prepared for CISA, Republic of Panama, October 1971. 26 pages.

Chiriquí Land Co. Hechos acerca del Negocio del Banano en Panamá. 1971. 12 pages.

Christian, James W. A Macro-Sectoral Survey of the Economy of Panama. Report prepared for MPPE, Republic of Panama, April 1970. 84 pages.

Colón-Tórres, Ramón. Evaluación de la Federación de Cooperativas Agropecuarias de Panamá—COAGRO. Servicios Técnicos del Caribe, San Juan, Puerto Rico, February 1973. 65 pages.

Córdoba, Teófilo; and Campos, José. Estudio sobre la Commercialización de Insumos Agropecuarios en Panamá. Report prepared for CISA, Republic of Panama, 1971. 127 pages.

Dirección General de Planificación y Administración. Evaluación Preliminar de los Recursos Agro-Físicos de la República de Panamá. Republic of Panama, September 1971. 94 pages.

———. Estudios Sectoriales: Sector Agropecuario. Republic of Panama, June 1970. 294 pages.

Fenton, Floyd. Quality and Standards for Milk in the Republic of Panama. Report prepared for MIDA, Republic of Panama, August 1972. 37 pages.

Facultad de Agronomía, Universidad de Panamá. Costos de Producción de Productos Agropecuarios. Report prepared for CISA, Republic of Panama, September 1971. 73 pages.

Fong, Nancy. El Sistema de Control de Precios en Panamá. Report prepared for CISA, Republic of Panama, January 1972. 16 pages.

———. Estudio de los Patrones de Consumo de Alimentos en la Ciudad de Panamá. Report prepared for CISA, Republic of Panama, March 1972. 35 pages.

———. Insumos Agropecuarios. Report prepared for CISA, Republic of Panama, February 1972. 50 pages.

———. Mercadeo de Frutas y Vegetales en Panamá. Report prepared for CISA, Republic of Panama, October 1971. 66 pages.

———. Potencial de Exportación de Productos Agropecuarios Panameños a la Zona del Canal. Report prepared for CISA, Republic of Panama, December 1971. 19 pages.

Fuéntes, Cándida. Observaciones sobre Costos de Producción y Problemas Técnicos del Cultivo de Algunas Hortalizas. Report prepared for CISA, Republic of Panama, December 1972. 37 pages.

Harberger, Arnold C. The Past Growth and Future Prospects of the Panamanian Economy. Report prepared for MPPE, Republic of Panama, June 1972. 36 pages.

Harel, Haim. Estudio sobre la Economía de la Producción Ganadera en Panamá, 1971. Technical Report #6, PANIO, United Nations (FAO), November 1972. 88 pages.

Herrmann, Louis. An Analysis of Livestock Production Prospects in Panama. Report prepared for MIDA, Republic of Panama, February 1973. 27 pages.

———. Beef and Milk Production and Marketing in Panama. Report prepared for CISA, Republic of Panama, December 1971. 22 pages.

Hoffmann, Randall A. Agricultural Sector Analysis and Planning, Panama. Report prepared for CISA, April 1971. 58 pages.

Instituto Interamericano de Ciencias Agrícolas de la OEA. Proyecto de Zonificación Ecológica de los Cultivos de Consumo Básicos y Tradicionales de Exportación de la República de Panamá en Condiciones de Secano. Turrialba, Costa Rica, December 1971. 58 pages.

IBRD. Memorandum on Recent Economic Developments and Prospects of Panama. Report CA-NA, July 1971.

Johnson, Harry G. Panama as a Regional Financial Center. Report prepared for MPPE, Republic of Panama, August 1972. 51 pages.

McClure, Charles E., Jr. The Distribution of Income and Tax Incidence in Panama, 1969. Report prepared for MPPE, Republic of Panama, August 1971. 80 pages.

Mackie, Arthur B. An Appraisal of Agricultural Export Potentials for Panama. Report prepared for CISA, Republic of Panama, February 1972. 24 pages.

Malcolm, John. Vegetables in Panama's Development Program—An Assessment and Recommendations. Report prepared for MIDA, Republic of Panama, February 1973. 48 pages.

Menchaca, Arnold. Development of Grades and Standards for Carcass Beef for Panama. Report prepared for MIDA, Republic of Panama, April 1972. 21 pages.

Ministerio de Agricultura y Ganadería. Guía para la Producción del Arroz, Maíz, Frijol y Tomate Industrial. Servicio Nacional de Investigación, Extensión y Educación Agropecuaria, Republic of Panama, 1971. 64 pages.

———. Organización Administrativa del Sector Agropecuario de Panamá. Republic of Panama, 1971. Vols. I and II. 415 pages.

———. Plan Nacional de Educación, Investigación y Extensión Agropecuaria, 1971–1976. Republic of Panama, 1971. Summary and 5 vols. 868 pages.

———. Programa Agropecuario. Republic of Panama, 1972. 60 pages. Anexo No. 1, Proyecciones. 13 pages.

Moreno, Juan Luís. Informe sobre la Matríz de Insumo-Producto. Report prepared for Contraloría General, Republic of Panama, November 1969. 14 pages.

Myren, Delbert T. Some Observations Related to Needs for Diffusion of Modern Production Methods in Panamanian Agriculture. Report prepared for MIDA, Republic of Panama, February 1973. 11 pages.

Ordaz, Beatríz. Estudio de la Política de Regulación de Precios y de la Metodología para la Fijación de Precios Máximos de la República de Panamá. Professional thesis, Faculty of Public Administration and Commerce, University of Panama, March 1972. 156 pages.

Organización Internacional del Trabajo. La Situación y Perspectivas del Empleo en Panamá. Report PRELAC/56, Vols. I, II, III, and IV, January 1973. 593 pages.

Pacheco, José; and Quiróz, Adolfo. Proyecciones de la Producción y de la Demanda de los Productos Agropecuarios. Technical Report, MAG, Republic of Panama, October, 1969. 41 pages.

Peacock, David. Price Variability in Panama for Three Vegetable Crops. Report prepared for CISA, Republic of Panama, 1971. 12 pages.

Phillips, Richard. Needs and Opportunities for Improved Grain Marketing in Panama during the Decade Ahead. Report 28, Food and Feed Grain Institute, Kansas State University, Manhattan, October 1971. 224 pages.

———. Improved Grain Marketing in Panama during the Decade Ahead. Report 36, Food and Feed Grain Institute, Kansas State University, Manhattan, March 1973. 44 pages.

Petruc, Teodoro. Tenencia de la Tierra en Panamá. Report prepared for CISA, Republic of Panama, December 1971. 95 pages.

Pitts, James E. Report and Recommendations on Agricultural Credit Systems in Panama. Report prepared for MIDA, Republic of Panama, February 1973. 39 pages.

Quiróz, Adolfo. Caña de Azúcar y Azúcar de Caña. Report prepared for CISA, Republic of Panama, April 1972. 34 pages.

———. Organización del Sector Agropecuario—Resumen. Report prepared for CISA, Republic of Panama, 1972. 37 pages.

———. Producción de Café en Panamá. Report prepared for CISA, Republic of Panama, March 1972. 28 pages.

Rappaport, Alan I. Macro-Economic Projections. Report prepared for MPPE, Republic of Panama, June 1972. 40 pages.

Rourke, J. Phillip. A Review and Appraisal of Factors Affecting Livestock Production in Panama. Report prepared for MIDA, Republic of Panama, February 1973. 24 pages.

Sahota, Gian S. Public Expenditure and Income Distribution in Panama. Report prepared for MPPE, Republic of Panama, August 1972. 242 pages.

Sites, John W.; Browning, Charles B.; and Popenoe, Hugh. Agricultural Research and Higher Education in Panama. Center for Tropical Agriculture,

Institute of Food and Agricultural Sciences, University of Florida, Gainesville, September 1971. 71 pages.

Sjaastad, Larry A. Prospects for Economic Growth in the 1970's: Panama. Report prepared for MPPE, Republic of Panama, March 1972. 43 pages.

Sosa, Humberto. Programa de Desarrollo Agropecuario 1969–74. Resumen. Análisis de la Situación y de los Problemas del Sector. Report prepared for MPPE, Republic of Panama, July 1969. 25 pages.

———. Sector Agropecuario, Diagnóstico de la Situación. Report prepared for MPPE, Republic of Panama, September 1968 (preliminary). 106 pages.

Stavrou, Jarilaos. Marco de Referencia Macroeconómico. Report prepared for MPPE, Republic of Panama, July 1972. 23 pages.

Swett, Charles. Agricultural Credit—Panama. Report prepared for CISA, Republic of Panama, May 1971. 44 pages.

———. Milk Production and Marketing in Panama. Report prepared for CISA, Republic of Panama, December 1971. 53 pages.

———. Poultry Production and Marketing in Panama. Report prepared for CISA, Republic of Panama, December 1971. 39 pages.

Taylor, Milton. Toward the Redistribution of Income in Panama. Report prepared for MPPE, Republic of Panama, August 1971. 13 pages.

Tejeira, Reinmar. Aspectos del Riego en Panamá. Asesoría Técnica, Panama City, June 1973.

United Nations (FAO). Inventariación y Demostraciones Forestales. Acopio y Transporte de Madera. Technical Report SF/PAN6, Rome, 1972. 67 pages.

———. Panamá-Inventariación y Demostraciones Forestales. Final Report SF/PAN6, Rome, 1973 (preliminary). 81 pages.

———. Proyecto Regional de Desarrollo Pesquero en Centro América. Rome, September 1972. 61 pages.

Wellhausen, E. J. A Proposal for a National Program in Rural Development Focused Primarily on Improving the Income and General Welfare of the Subsistence of Semi-Commercial Farmers and Underemployed Rural Laborers in Panama. Report prepared for MIDA, Republic of Panama, April 1973 (preliminary). 46 pages.

INDEX